DISCOVERERS OF BLOOD CIRCULATION

From Aristotle to the Times of Da Vinci and Harvey

The Life of Science Library 40

DISCOVERERS OF

From Aristotle to the

ABELARD - SCHUMAN LONDON •

BLOOD CIRCULATION

Times of Da Vinci and Harvey

BY T. DOBY, M. D.

Preface by John F. Fulton, late professor of the History of Medicine, Yale University

NEW YORK   •   TORONTO

LONDON   NEW YORK   TORONTO

Abelard-Schuman Limited   Abelard-Schuman Limited   Abelard-Schuman Canada Limited

8 King Street   6 West 57th Street   896 Queen Street

CONTENTS

■

LIST OF ILLUSTRATIONS

■

List of Illustrations

PREFACE

■

In keeping with the best tradition of historical writing, Dr. Doby
has given us in this volume a straightforward account, in language that can be read by layman, doctor, or the more mature
historian of medicine with sheer pleasure. Coming from a country
in which historical approaches to medicine and science have long
been cultivated, he brings the fresh point of view of a European
scholar. But he gives more than this, for he provides us with many
new and original illustrations never before seen in the historical
literature of physiology.

The book contains a sensitive and discriminating study of the
lives and labours of the great forerunners, contemporaries and
followers of William Harvey. The personalities of these men in
many ways are as interesting as the discoveries that they made.
The literature of the discovery of circulation is replete with repe-
titious accounts, often based on secondary sources. Dr. Doby on
the contrary in every case has studied original texts, partly in
Europe, partly at Yale University. His book thus forms a fitting
companionpiece to the excellent studies of Dr. K. J. Franklin on

Fabricius ab Acquapendente and his *De Ostiolis Venarum* and Dr. Franklin's later translations of the works of Harvey himself.

It is a pleasure to welcome this book as a valuable contribution to the history of medicine.

Yale University, 1960   JOHN F. FULTON, M.D.

INTRODUCTION

■

Hundreds of thousands of people die every year of heart disease, and the number is rising. While contagious diseases are becoming less and less a menace because of new remedies, each one of us is faced with the increasing possibility of acquiring some form of circulatory disease sooner or later. Yet we need not be discouraged. Year after year, as our knowledge broadens, more ways of combatting circulatory disease are discovered.

But it is interesting that only in very recent times have we really dared to touch the heart itself; and now we cut it, sew it up, and not infrequently almost rebuild it. We are able to cure, or at any rate, correct disorders which formerly would have caused certain death. As for the future, there is every hope that more lives will be saved through heart surgery and other means, means our parents and grandparents would never have dreamed possible. Still, there is irony in the fact that we take such recent achievements for granted and that we do not even stop to consider that our knowledge of the nature of blood circulation—the basis for all our present progress—is also rather recent.

Those who discovered the mysteries of circulation did not work in comfortable laboratories, supported by generous grants of money and encouraged by the approval of everyone around them, like our scientists today. They had to overcome the barriers of suspicion, superstition, hatred. And if, in spite of these barriers their passion spurred them on to seek new knowledge, they could expect nothing but persecution, imprisonment, or at best ridicule. And all this because they dared to think as we do today.

Who were these people who succeeded in discovering the truth about the "mysteries" of the blood and its circulation? What circumstances helped them in their quest and what hindered them? How far did they progress and where did they fall in error? How did they live?

These were the men who gave us our knowledge of ourselves. They made it clear to us what an infinitesimal part we are of the laws of creation, which are at work within us without our even noticing them. Having acquainted us with these laws, they gave us the possibility of regulating them in case they should turn against us.

This book is about these men, their problems and their joys, their stumblings and their triumphs, and about the secrets which they spent their lives discovering.

DISCOVERERS OF BLOOD CIRCULATION

From Aristotle to the Times of Da Vinci and Harvey

HIGHLIGHTS IN

	History	Science and Technology	Medicine
400-300 B.C.	Alexander the Great's Egyptian and Middle Eastern conquest (337-23). Greek cultural influence in Mediterranean area.	Platonic Academy founded (Athens 387). Globular shape of earth, speed of falling objects, magnetism, etc., taught (Aristotle, 384-22).	Clinical observations without mystic overtones (Hippocrates, around 400). Comparative anatomy, classification of species, developmental experiments (Aristotle).
300-200 B.C.	Dynasty of Ptolemies in Egypt. Library of Alexandria founded (around 300). Rome's Punic wars (264-41; 218-01).	Geometry of Euclid (270). Heliocentric system described (Aristarchus, 270). Mechanical machines (Archimedes, 250; Hero, 230). Calculation of π (Archimedes, 240).	Dissection of humans in Alexandria (around 300-250). Distinction of vessels and nerves (Herophilus, 280). Brain center of intelligence, valves in heart, their role to direct blood described (Erasistratus, 260).
200-100 B.C.	Third Punic war, Carthage's destruction (146). Expansion of Rome. Military road networks built by Rome.	Lightning rod known (180). Ecliptic (Erathosthenes, 220), precession (Hipparchus, 160) made known.	Decline of scientific medicine; scholastic discussions, fruitless theories.

HIGHLIGHTS IN

	History	Science and Technology	Medicine
100-1 B.C.	Caesar's struggle for might. Destruction of Alexandrian Library (47). Death of Caesar; civil war in Rome (44-31). Augustus is emperor (31 B.C.-14 A.D.).	Shorthand invented (Tiro, 50); daily public news reports (Caesar, 45). Natural science encyclopedia (Varro, 45). War and construction machines described (Vitruvius, 13).	Public health improved in Roman Empire: aqueducts built, reservoirs used (daily water consumption per person, 100 gallons in Rome), canalization.
1-100 A.D.	Revolt in Judea (66-70), destruction of Jerusalem by Romans (70). Spread of Christian faith and persecutions. Roman campaigns against barbarian tribes.	Natural history encyclopedia (Pliny, 70). Glass mirror and lenses known (around 100).	Medical encyclopedia with descriptions of numerous surgical equipment and procedures (Celsus, 35).
100-200 A.D.	Inner peace and greatest welfare in Rome until death of Marcus Aurelius (180). Devastating plague and Great Migration shaking Roman civilization.	Geographic map with meridians (Ptolemy, 155); refraction of light, astronomical system described (Ptolemy). Machine-moved carriage of Emperor Commodus mentioned in contemporary reports (170).	Medical encyclopedia by Galen, based on personal observation, experiments in physiology (pulsation of arteries, nerve supply of muscles, function of kidneys, etc.).

CHAPTER ONE

ERASISTRATUS IN ALEXANDRIA

■

Are great intellectual achievements the fruits of thought alone? To what extent do chance and environment play a role in such achievements?

From the writings of Plato and Aristotle, or the thoughts revealed in Cicero's letters, we see that the deductions these and other ancients made concerning a given problem was often no different from what our own would have been. How is it possible, then, that our factual information today should be so much greater and more accurate, when man's intelligence and his universal traits which make for moodiness, doubt, curiosity and the desire to know remain unchanged?

First, of course, the methods with which we seek solutions have greatly changed since ancient times. Surely it is the different sets of attitudes, assumptions, intellectual and non-intellectual habits which distinguish one person or group from another, even though all are trying to solve the same problem with equal intelligence and potentiality.

But behind the significance of method and attitude, seemingly spurious factors often prove to be crucial.

When the Babylonians, Chinese and Egyptians already boasted a high level of culture, the Greeks were still leading the simple lives of shepherds. Yet the Greeks came to surpass the older established civilizations; and it is almost exclusively to the ancient Greeks that we must revert in order to study our generic topic, the development of medical science in the Western world.

The Greeks owed the development of their intellectual life not only to their innate abilities, but particularly to two important factors. In Greece the priestly functions were performed by ordinary citizens serving for short periods of time on an honorary basis. There was no chance for lifelong power or enrichment and therefore little impetus for force and fanaticism to rise up under the protective shield of the priesthood. The religion of the boldly argumentative and readily cheerful Greeks seldom demanded blind unshakable faith. Because the mythology stemmed from secular men, the priestly caste, with its stiff rituals and jealous obstructionism, which hindered the progress of other nations, was absent here. Thus it was possible for the Greeks to discuss, examine and question many phenomena without offending their deities.

Nevertheless, the sparks emanating from free intellects would have been quickly extinguished had it not been for eight small symbols. The Greeks completed the written alphabet taken over from the Phoenicians. They had only to learn twenty-seven letters in order to bring at will articulate thoughts to their lives. There was no need to see vowels to go with the empty-sounding consonants, as did the Phoenicians, nor did they need to trace out 500 difficult pictograms, like the Egyptian scribes, or 600, like the Sumerians, or several thousand, like the Chinese. The Greeks expressed everything with their twenty-seven letters; thus not only the scholar could learn them, but the merchant and the soldier as well. The opinions of the wise men, the latest lyric poem or the result of the Olympic games were accessible to a large segment of the population. A surprising number could read and write.

It was as easy to make a note of the most profound wisdom as of the most impossible absurdities which aroused the protests of many people, thus leading to endless arguments, libel, and criticism—in other words, to the intellectual life, the seeds of which eventually blossomed into art and science.

* * *

When Erasistratus, son of the physician at the court of Antioch, was born (ca. 320 B.C.), Greek culture was at its height. Syrian Antioch was one of the great capitals of the world. King Seleucus Nicator, who had been a cavalry general under Alexander the Great in the Indian campaign, surrounded himself with much pomp which, in his new office, he felt was his due. He was ruler of an enormous empire, extending from Syria to the Indies.

But Seleucus Nicator exerted himself in vain: Athens remained the center of intellectual life, although in political importance and number of inhabitants Antioch far surpassed it.

As was customary, Erasistratus followed his father's profession. The son of the empire's foremost physician had to receive the best of educations and this could only be obtained on the Greek peninsula. A distinguished young man in Athens was expected to master many things, from logic and the verses of Homer to athletics, from oratory to moral conduct—everything, in fact, which was supposed to make a man excel intellectually, physically and spiritually.

In the gymnasium the young man could watch the achievements of the Olympic athletes, and could practice his skill at wrestling, boxing or running. The bath followed, then the massage, to enable him to pursue with renewed freshness the knowledge of his chosen field.

At the medical school, one of Erasistratus's masters was Methrodorus, the third husband of Aristotle's daughter. Certainly through Methrodorus the students received a definitive teaching of the great master's views. Some years earlier the aged Aristotle himself walked with his students in the park surrounding Apollo's temple, and presided over this school which was established for him from funds given by Alexander the Great.

There was a zoological garden attached to the school, to which agents sent back every imaginable animal from the four corners of the earth, from colorful birds to reptiles and apes. Under Aristotle's direction these expeditions for the collection

1. Aristotle. (By unknown Greek contemporary. Copy in Museum of the Therme in Rome.)

of specimens also made geographical and astronomical observations. *

While plant and animal specimens were meticulously collected and classified, it was also quite usual to dissect the muscles and organs of animals to try to force nature, by means of experiments, to reveal the workings of life. Aristotle was not only interested in factual findings, but in the processes which made things the way they were.

An excellent subject for the study of the development of the organism proved to be the egg. A better one has still not been found. Aristotle's aim was to observe how the liquid mass of a freshly laid egg turned into a winged, chirping little chick. For a time nothing would be visible except the formless, opaque jelly, until on the fourth day a small red spot appeared, which pulsated from time to time. The spot a few days later grew until it became apparent that the chick's heart was, visibly, being created before his eyes. Having observed full-grown animals of various species Aristotle had long noticed that the heart occupied a position in the middle of the trunk.

The heart is created first, the heart is the last organ to stop working, the heart is in the center of the body, therefore the conclusion seemed clear to him: the heart is the seat of life.

But do not the heart beats speed up or slow down when a man experiences joy or sorrow? From this Aristotle concluded that desires, feelings, in fact, all emotions are derived from the heart. So much so that the voice, the expression of all these, had to originate from the heart also.

The brain seemed to him to represent the direct opposite of the warm, mobile, blood-filled heart. It was cool, contained little blood and was immobile; therefore he concluded that its function was to cool the blood heated by the violent exertions of the heart. However, he believed the soul, the intellect, and the character were not bound to any organ; they were independent of the body.

The heart, Aristotle said, was not merely the main conductor of movement and emotions, but also the controller of metabo-

---

*For example, he deduced that the earth must be global, because the shadow of the earth cut crescent-shaped slices off the moon.

lism. The substances absorbed from nutrition, he thought,
turned into blood in the heart and there mixed with air, or
pneuma, which came from the lungs. And what was the function of air? Again, since it was cold, its purpose was to cool
the hot blood.

Aristotle's successors, among them Methrodorus, taught these
views to the young generation, and this is how Erasistratus acquired his knowledge. In addition to education in theory, he
received quite early much practical instruction. He had to sit
at the bedside of a patient, study the patient's facial expression, his way of lying down, the moisture of his skin, the
size of his pupils; he had to examine stools and urine. He had
to make notes on everything in order that on his return
some days later he should be able to make comparison with
his earlier observations. Body temperature was determined by
a hand placed on the chest, heartbeats were evaluated by touch.
The abdomen was prodded to see whether there was any en-
largement of spleen or liver. The patient was made to sit up
and was shaken by the shoulders to detect any possible sound
of fluid which would point to pus in the chest cavity. If the
tell-tale sound was heard, knives and forceps were brought
out and the fluid was drained off. If there was nothing present,
the physician had to bend over the patient and listen with
ear pressed to the back to determine whether the pleura made
any sounds, or whether there was whistling from the lungs.

Once Erasistratus had mastered these procedures, he received the distinction of being allowed to accompany his master to an occasional rich patient. On such expeditions he carried
the little wooden chest containing the instruments required for
probing or stitching, together with a few empty garlic shells
to measure the depth of abcesses. The contents also included a
catheter, rectal mirror, knife, forceps and a small home dis-
pensary.

Erasistratus was young and appears to have believed firmly
in the Hippocratic saying: "The physician, be he a philosopher
also, is akin to the Gods."

                          *   *   *

Although Hippocrates was constantly quoted, his teachings
were not accepted with undivided enthusiasm in Athens. Some

accused him of vanity and selfishness and of setting fire to the
library of the medical school in Cos in order to remain the
sole fountainhead of medical knowledge. As for Methrodoros,
teacher of Erasistratus, he had studied in Cnidus in his younger
days, which in itself tended to dispose him against Hippocrates.

For the aim of the Cnidian School was to attribute each
disease to changes in one single organ. Thus Methrodorus
sought local causative factors as opposed to the Hippocratic
School, which claimed that the cause of disease was to be found
in the faulty distribution of the fluids present in every part of
the body. But many of his colleagues favored Hippocrates, although they might differ from him in matters of detail. Euryphon, for instance, maintained that as a result of excessive food
consumption superfluous nourishment rose into the head, causing illness. He also taught that bleeding could be caused not
only by an injury to veins, but to arteries also, which Aristotle
had denied, believing that the arteries contained not blood, but
air.

Exposed to so many conflicting viewpoints, Erasistratus
wished to hear at first hand the teachings of Hippocrates. He
therefore sailed from Cnidus to the little island of Cos, situated
close to the mainland. Its pleasant climate drew thousands to
the shrine of Asclepius, god of healing. At the medical school,
just as in Cnidos, an extensive library and famous professors
were at the disposal of the students. As a result Erasistratus
gained an increasingly broad outlook.

He had to learn how the physician should approach his patient with a dignified bearing to gain his confidence, how he
should listen patiently to the sick man's complaints, what great
care must be exercised not to spoil his reputation by a hastily-
given opinion. For "Life is short and the art long; the occasion
fleeting; experience fallacious, and judgment difficult."

He had to study the properties of the four chief fluids: the
blood, the "yellow bile," the "black bile" and phlegm; also the
symptoms occurring when their balance was disturbed. His attention was drawn to the importance of heredity and environment and the frequency of certain diseases in summer and others
in winter. He had to learn the names of innumerable purgatives and emetics and learned also that the best way to remove

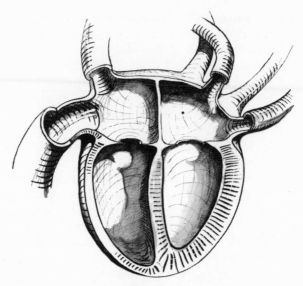

2. *Schematic picture of cross section of auricles and ventricles. (By A. Barabas)*

harmful fluids was by blood letting. How else, after all, could one possibly be rid of the evil "hot and dry" black bile and the "cool and moist" phlegm?

The students dissected animals, never humans. It would have been considered sacrilege to touch a dead man. After having opened the chest and inspected the lungs, they would then examine the heart. When the thick outer wall of the heart was cut open they found two chambers within, one situated more to the left, the other to the right: in other words, the left and right ventricles. But above each of these they found a chamber with a thinner wall: the left and right auricles. These they took to be extensions of the blood vessels leading into them, of no special significance.

The left and right sides were separated by a muscular partition. They found but little blood in the left ventricle and the vessel leading from it; the latter was largely empty or "filled with air," which is why it was named "aorta," or air transmitter. This blood vessel, thicker than a thumb, had three small valves

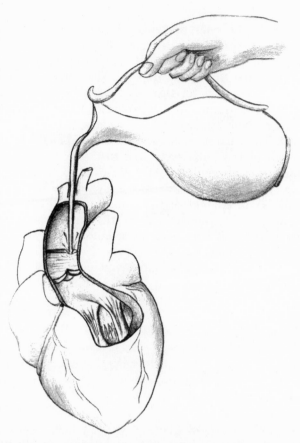

3. *When water is poured into the aorta, the valves close and the water cannot flow back into the heart. This experiment was known already before Hippocrates. (By S. Magyar)*

closing towards the ventricle and opening in the opposite direction. The function of these valves was known long before Erasistratus. In fact, it was written in one of the earliest Greek medical papers, before Hippocrates and Aristotle, that "if the heart is removed and the valves are drawn up from the wall of the aorta towards the center, neither air nor water can penetrate into the heart."

In Cos, Erasistratus soon began to hear new theories not

consistent with the ones previously known. Praxagoras taught that the arteries contracted rhythmically and that this was felt in the form of pulse beats, which the other schools had not even distinguished from body tremors. This view was as logical as preceding ones, and for this very reason aroused doubts in the mind of Erasistratus. For, according to Praxagoras the aorta contained air, while according to Euryphon it contained blood. Praxagoras held that the pulsations of the blood vessels felt at the touch of the pulse were due to the actual contractions of the blood vessels, whereas Aristotle claimed these were due to the extension of impulses caused by the bubbling of the air and the small amount of blood inside the heart. Who was right? Only lengthy personal observation and experimentation could convince Erasistratus; only personal experiences could create order out of such chaos. However, he had already spent many years away from his country, and presumably his father wished to see his clever son at home, to introduce him to the intricacies of a medical practice at court. He had to return to Antioch.

We know nothing about the first few years he spent at home; in fact our information about his personal life is generally scanty. But we do know that before long he emerged in fame in connection with an interesting family scandal whose leading figure was Antiochus, the son of the King.

*   *   *

For a time the young prince Antiochus had been suffering from a curious malady. He wandered listlessly, or lay for days at a time in the palace rooms, hardly touching his food. He became silent and withdrawn. He lost weight, his skin became moistly pale and it seemed as though nothing would help him, not the whole mass of Indian miracle drugs, or the diets usual in such cases, or even the sacrifices made to the god Asclepius.

On one occasion Erasistratus was standing beside the heir apparent's bed, thoughtfully feeling his pulse, trying to discern the nature of the mysterious disease, when someone quietly entered the room. Both of them looked up. Erasistratus bowed, but did not relinquish the patient's wrist. In that moment the pulse itself revealed the nature of the "consuming malady" — love!

The blood vessel, which until then had fluttered very feebly suddenly began to throb violently. The pale face became pink, and the patient sighed deeply as he gazed at his visitor. The seventy-year-old king's radiant young wife had entered. The illness of Antiochus was indeed quite serious: he was in love with his stepmother!

Thus his father, the great ruler, the conquering warrior, suffered an odd defeat. And, great as he was as a triumphant military commander, the king proved equally great in these sad moments: he gave up his wife and sent her away with his son to govern a distant section of the empire (293 B.C..)

Nevertheless, court life in Antioch became no more peaceful for his action.

Besides Seleucus, Alexander the Great had had two other generals who became rulers of vast empires after his death: Lysimachus in Western Asia Minor and Ptolemy in Egypt. The trouble began when the aging Ptolemy started to feel his strength ebbing and appointed his favorite son, that of his second wife, to rule beside him, thus bypassing his elder son. Not two years after their father's death (284 B.C.) the pent-up hostilities between the two brothers broke out.

The elder, Ceraunus, was obliged to flee and hopefully went to Seleucus in Antioch. Seleucus immediately saw the opportunities offered by the confusing state of affairs. It gave him a chance to occupy the rival empire of Egypt with the legitimate excuse of protector of the exiled. In spite of his eighty-three years he wanted to accomplish what Alexander the Great had failed to do with the energy of his youth: he wanted to unite the world.

Seleucus made strategic plans for the occupation of Egypt. Meanwhile, Ceraunus realized that should Seleucus win, not he but Seleucus would succeed his father. In bitter resentment he killed the aged King.

It seems probable that the close entourage of Seleucus, including Erasistratus, cannot have enjoyed any great measure of personal safety during those days. There is no record of it, but in all likelihood it was soon after Seleucus' death that Erasistratus left Antioch. Under the circumstances Erasistratus could expect safety in one place only: with the enemy of Ceraunus, with the young Ptolemy in Alexandria.

※ ※ ※

Situated in the Nile Delta, Alexandria was the focal point for caravans plying between India and Phoenicia, the flourishing Greek islands and, increasingly, powerful Rome. Eastern perfumes, Carthaginian glassware and textiles changed hands there. From Alexandria grain for Rome was shipped. Its thriving ship-building industry produced excellent cedarwood craft ranging in size from fishing smacks to sea-going galleys with three rows of oars.

The possibility of enrichment had attracted to Alexandria the descendants of Jews, who had remained scattered in Egypt instead of following Moses on his desert journey, as well as Greek traders from Samos and Cyprus and Egyptian clerks from Thebes and Memphis.

On the site of a small fishing village new palaces rose. A vast harbor was built, and at the end of the longest jetty, among a few squat warehouses and churches, a tall tower stood out as a landmark to navigators. This lighthouse could be seen some forty miles away by a sailor on look-out, and at night torches flaming on its tower showed the way.

The Royal Palace was, of course, built in the Greek style; with the harbor adjoining, it made up the heart of the city. Immediately beside the Palace was the Museum, the City of Science. The Library was its center. It was housed in an imposing building flanked on either side by a row of columns, with marble memorials at the entrance to the old Ptolemy and to the scholar Demetrius. These two had planned the entire City of Science and had succeeded in creating an institution which was far greater and more enduring than the Aristotelian Academy.

We have no record of the interior arrangements but have some data concerning the uses and division of the various buildings. One pavilion was reserved for the translation and copying of collected documents. A crowd of clerks sat around here painting Greek letters onto scrolls eighty to one hundred yards long and ten to twenty inches wide. Artists added illustrations with India ink and yellow, red, and green paint. The originals and the translations were then placed in the rooms of the Library.

Copies were sent to the "Serapion" (Temple of the God Serapis) situated in a different part of the city, which served as a branch to the main library.

In another building the scholars had their living quarters, comfortably furnished, 'and with a sufficient number of slaves. The baths and athletic fields were close by.

An out-patients' department, an autopsy room, smaller premises for experimentation, large lecture halls, and towers suitable for astronomical observation, as well as zoological and botanical gardens completed this scientific institute, which in toto occupied an entire section of the capital.

This was where Erasistratus found himself in the prime of his life.

By day, life in the city with its million inhabitants went on apparently without friction. But at night the three nationalities, the Jewish ex-slaves, the Egyptian ex-rulers, and the conquering Greeks, retired to their own sections of the city, each group hating and fearing the other two.

The Egyptians resented the Greeks and despised them. What an upstart culture was theirs compared to the Egyptians! The priests, moreover, feared the Greeks. Egyptian history had shown that obedience to new gods brought only disaster. The priests knew that their privileges, power, their very existence, could be maintained only if they could mold the foreigners into Egyptians and make them break away from the ideals and religion which made them rulers. In such matters the Egyptian priests turned out to be successful diplomats.

They had curried favor with Alexander the Great by spreading the rumor that he was not the son of Philip of Macedon, but descended directly from the god Amon, which so flattered the vain Alexander that he is said to have died believing it himself. Similarly, they tried to influence Ptolemy, but here their attempts met with eventual failure. Instead of old Memphis, he made the new city of Alexandria his capital, and to give added importance to his action he had Alexander's embalmed body brought there from its famous place of pilgrimage of Siwa.

Alexandria had grown into a rich center, pushing into the background others which had led in importance: Corinth in

Greece and Carthage in Phoenicia. Its inhabitants boasted that
most cities grow out of their immediate surroundings, but that
Alexandria grew from the entire world.

* * *

At the western outskirts of the city was a road bordered
with sparsely-growing palms.

The ibis, birds of the goddess Isis, stretched their long necks
in search of fish in the water of the canal. Here and there
a mausoleum rose out of the ground, and even the simpler
graves were thickly strewn with flowers.

This was the Necropolis, the City of the Dead.

Here, at the final rites for the deceased, mourning relatives
wore white clothing. Weeping women, among them the priest,
offered prayers to Osiris, god of the world beyond.

The paraschistes, a priestly official, stepped forward and drew
a line on the left side of the body's bare abdomen. Another
one advanced and, with a single thrust from a stone knife,
cut through the abdominal wall at the place indicated—then,
casting his knife away he fled. A hail of stones was thrown
after him. This symbolic stoning was part of the ritual, serving
to warn those present of the consequences of robbing the dead
or looting the graves. And this was necessary since every one
knew that this was a regular source of additional income for the
grave diggers.

The funeral attendants now opened the abdomen, removed
the stomach and the intestines and placed them in a high-necked
vase. The spleen and kidney were put in another, the liver in
a third and finally, the heart and lungs were placed in a fourth.
Each vase was closed with a lid depicting one of the demons
of death. The heart, for instance, was guarded by the monkey's
head of Hapi. Inside the heart was put a small carved scarab.

The scarab beetle is a black insect which swarms by the
thousand in deserted dark holes, particularly if there is food
at hand. And since it was the custom to place the dead person's
favorite dishes and drinks beside him in the grave, everywhere
around the graves a mass of these silent, creeping scarab beetles
could be seen, which led the Egyptians to conclude that they
must somehow play an important role in the spirit life of their
deceased relations.

4. *The four canopi from left to right: Mesti, Hapi, Duamutef, Queb-senuf, guarding the liver, heart, lung and stomach with intestines. (From R. A. Martin: Mummies.)*

5. *Heart scarab top side and under side. The hieroglyphs on it describe the prayer addressed to the heart. (Budapest, Museum of Fine Arts.)*

6. *18th Dynasty illustration of the Theban papyrus scroll from the Book of the Dead. Jackal-headed God Anubis weighs the heart with a feather mark, symbol of Goddess of Justice Maat, while ibis-headed Toth records the result. (R. A. Martin: Mummies)*

Besides the symbolic scarab, a papyrus scroll was also placed in the heart, containing a prayer:
"Heart by my mother given
Heart of my being,
Do not rise against me on judgment day,
Do not bear witness against me at the time of my reckoning,
Do not gainsay me before those assembled,
Do not vote against me before the guardian of the Steps . . .
Do not make my name abhorred by the Gods."
The preparation of the body was nearly completed. The assistants pierced the skull through the nose with a bronze hook just over a hand's length, and adroitly scraped out the brain.

The body thus prepared was taken to the vicinity of the temple, lowered into a pit and covered with sodium carbonate solution. It was kept there for seventy days, after which it was raised and dried in the hot desert sun. The inside was washed with palm wine, then saturated with the smoke of incense and myrrh.

After this the body was stuffed with bandages soaked in cassia, cedar resin and asphalt. The limbs and the torso were tightly bound, a painted mask was placed upon the face, and the body was put into a wooden coffin. The mummy was ready to be held up for the final reckoning before the ultimate judge, Osiris, and ready to follow Amon Ra's call at the time of the resurrection.

The priest made sure that the ritual was carried out with precision and gave instructions, but he never touched the body. Dynasty followed dynasty during several thousand years, Persians and Greeks might drive the country into subjection, but the ritual did not change. Never would an Egyptian priest step closer to the opened human body, to see whether it was as he imagined it.

The priests differed greatly from the other inhabitants of Egypt. A short white apron hung from their waists; their chests and backs were bare. Only for funerals did they throw a leopard skin over their shoulders. They gave meticulous attention to the hands and face. They bathed twice, by day and by night, giving a striking impression of cleanliness and freshness in that hot climate. They shaved their heads and faces, and every third day the rest of their bodies. They were careful to observe the rule, which actually applied to all of the inhabitants, of taking purgatives for three days every month, and a dose of emetics, to cleanse themselves internally.

Their physical cleanliness and distinctive clothing were only the outward signs of their almost limitless power and their knowledge. They were not only masters of the mysteries of Osiris, of the laws of the country, astronomy and engineering, but some of them were also trained as physicians at the schools of Memphis and Sais. They knew that the heart was the starting point of the vascular system and they taught that air streamed into the lungs through "the thirty two vessels" in the head, and from there into the heart. The various threadlike systems branching throughout the body were pictured as consisting of tubes, whether these were blood vessels, nerves or something else.

Disease, they thought, was associated almost exclusively with over-eating or drinking; hence the regimen of fasting, purging and dieting. The medications included hippopotamus fat and lizard blood, and painting with vulture feathers was considered very effective, especially if certain prescribed magic formulae were murmured at the same time.

They were convinced that these ancient teachings and customs assured Egypt's superiority. Anyone deviating from them would have been considered a traitor.

* * *

From his writings it is plain that Erasistratus regarded Egyptian mysticism with contempt or amusement. But the majority of the Greek merchants, clerks, actors and athletes in Alexandria thought otherwise. There were so many things of which they boasted which the Egyptians claimed to have possessed long ago. This superior attitude aroused their respect and even led to imitation: it became fashionable to live the Egyptian way—even to die like the Egyptians. Many Greeks had their relatives embalmed. They stood around tearfully hour after hour, sweltering in the heat, watching the ritual. At first they shuddered, but later became increasingly curious. Soon they even ceased to be repelled by the dissection of the body.

Spurred by curiosity, Erasistratus, in possession of a royal permit, himself dissected the unburied bodies of criminals and beggars. He never felt himself demeaned by doing this, as did his Egyptian colleagues.

Since his rival's downfall, young Ptolemy, now able to rule in peace, encouraged investigations of this kind. In fact, he is even said to have permitted those condemned to death to be dissected alive "to allow the actual mechanism and color of various organs to be observed." This however, is by no means a proven fact. It is rather suspicious that the accusation emerged much later and originated from people anxious to discredit the Alexandrian School. Such were Celsus, from the Roman point of view, and Tertullianus, the church patriarch, who considered any endeavor to learn the secrets of nature as sacrilegious, not to say harmful. But even if the practice did exist, we must not forget that the slaves were not considered as equal human beings and that they were daily subjected to the most incredible exploitation and abuse. When they were being punished, pity or compassion towards them was simply unknown.

Supposing, therefore, that Ptolemy had really favored such grue-some torture as live dissection, we must pause to consider whether this was any more cruel than the usual methods of execution of robbers, murderers or escaped slaves, by drowning, beating to death or crucifixion.

Irrespective of this, Ptolemy was a man of wide and unusual interests. Like his father he was a first-rate general. He occupied Abyssinia, then started looking toward the southern shores of Arabia, meanwhile raising Egypt's industry and trade to hitherto unknown heights. But, when not occupied with affairs of state or war, he spent his free time in the Museum, among his scholars.

He was no dilettante. He collected and studied rare plants and animals. Occasionally he visited the dissecting room and himself peeled the skin off the body, curious about what lay beneath the visible shell. He did not behave in the ways prescribed by Greek custom or the rigid Egyptian code. He married his younger sister, like the ancient Pharaohs (which is why he was known as Philadelphus, or sister lover), to the extreme dismay of the Greeks. He opened the gates of scholarship to many previously excluded, in spite of the disapproval of the Egyptian priests. He maintained the cult of Amon and Serapis, had the shrines of Hathor and Ptah renovated, but at the same time allowed freedom of speech to other races and religions. At the scientific conferences he presided not as the descendant of the god Amon, but as an investigator among investigators, listening to the bold views presented.

It was at these gatherings that Euclid described his geometry and optics. During this period for the first time Aristarchus proposed that the earth was not the center of the Universe but a small planet belonging to the sun and revolving around it. And during this period, too, the internal mechanism of the human body was first discussed sensibly, objectively and un-emotionally. All this was taking place in the years around 260 B.C.

Herophilus, who was the grandson of Aristotle, was there also, presenting his views on health and disease. Herophilus was an ardent disciple of Hippocrates, believing that if a man were ill, his entire organism was diseased and that it was impossible to designate a specific origin of the disease: in other words, that

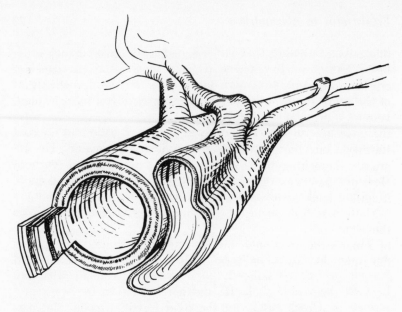

7. *Cross section of an artery and a vein. (By A. Barabas)*

all suffering was due to the faulty distribution of fluids. No matter who was brought to him for examination, he immediately felt the pulse, assuming that from its behavior he could determine the nature of any sort of trouble. He read much finer shades of difference into various actions of the pulse than had been usual up to then.

It was just at that time that an engineer perfected the water clock, and Herophilus hastened to make use of this new device for measuring the pulse rate. He studied the rhythm for several minutes at a time and if it was not regular, he tried to match it to the beat of harp or flute-playing provided by slave women.

He observed on living animals, or possibly men under sentence of death, that the thin white threads starting out from the muscles did not behave alike. With his experiments it was he who first differentiated between tendons and nerves, which until then were believed to be the same.

Herophilus also observed the heart and the blood vessels leading from it. Two types could be differentiated according to the thickness of the walls. One type was so thin that after the blood had run out of it, it deflated, and could be kneaded, crushed and twisted. These vessels all came from the right side of the heart and from there branched out into increasingly small vessels, until they finally vanished in the abdomen, the skin, the muscles: these were the veins. The thick blood vessels starting from the left side of the heart, the aorta and the arteries branching out from it, had thick, elastic walls; and Herophilus noticed that if he pressed one and then released it, it sprang back immediately to its original shape.

There was just one exception among the veins starting from the right side: there was one blood vessel, of the thickness of a man's thumb, which, although it led toward the lungs from the right side, was yet thick and elastic. No matter how hard

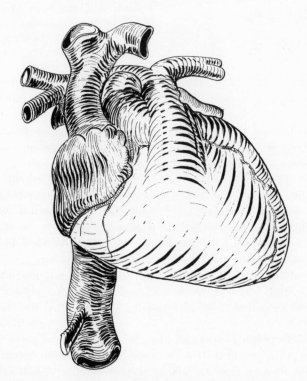

8. *Right half of the heart showing the large veins and the "artery-like vein", now called pulmonary artery. (By A. Barabas)*

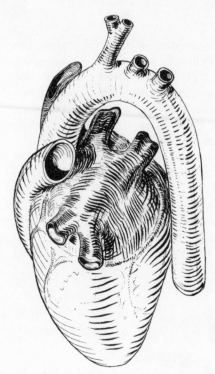

9. *Left side of the heart with the aorta and the "vein-like arteries", at present known as pulmonary veins. (By A. Barabas)*

he tried to twist it out of shape, when he released it, it resumed its normal shape. He studied the different layers of its wall and succeeded in peeling off six different layers, just as in the arteries. Thus, this one blood vessel, although it started from the right side of the heart, like the veins, behaved like an artery. Herophilus therefore named this exceptional vein "the artery-like vein" (now called the pulmonary artery).

But there was an exception on the left side, too. Certain blood vessels which connected the left auricle with the lungs, although they were situated on the left side, like the elastic and tougher arteries, had walls as weak and inelastic as the veins. These he therefore called "vein-like arteries" (now called the pulmonary veins).

Since Herophilus explained disease by the faulty distribution of fluids and the accumulation of black bile or phlegm, what could be more obvious than to release these from the vessels conveying them, that is, from the veins, by blood-letting? The sicker the man, the more the harmful fluid had accumulated, the more blood-letting had to be used. What of the patient, who meanwhile turned pale, broke into a cold sweat, fainted? He would soon recover once he had got rid of his harmful fluids.

Erasistratus for his part was of a different opinion. He did not in the least believe that the fluids were the sole sources of every disease. If careful observations were made, one found a change sometimes in the liver, sometimes in the lungs, or some other organ. For instance, the liver of anyone who had died of snake bite was of a soft, doughy consistency. If, on the other hand, the deceased patient's legs were swollen twice their size because of the fluid in them, the liver proved to be hard. Another interesting fact was that if straw-colored liquid streamed out when the chest cavity was opened, and if the otherwise smooth surface of the lungs was rough, then superfluous fluid would be found within the pericardium (sac enclosing the heart) as well. There were enough local symptoms present without requiring that one blame everything on the general disturbance of vague Hippocratical fluids.

And the blood-letting! It was quite impossible to determine how much harmful fluid there was in any patient and thus how much blood should be let in order to rid him of what was superfluous. Erasistratus considered unlimited blood-letting senseless, and actually harmful.

Then there was that exaggerated pulse cult practiced by Herophilus. In spite of its apparent correctness, was all this not somewhat extravagant and theoretical?

Erasistratus could not believe in Herophilus.

When he bent over a body with his knife and forceps, the picture he saw differed from that seen by his rival. He was able to detach himself from immediate contact with organs seen and touched, and without missing any details, could regard them, and their interconnection from, as it were, a height. He considered everything from the point of view of form and function — the smallest particle and at the same time the great whole.

He observed that the surface of the brain of cats and dogs was smoother than that of monkeys and that the convolutions of the monkey's brain were less numerous than those of humans. He concluded that the intellect was in some way connected with these convolutions. He discerned that some nerves conduct chiefly movement, while others only sensations.

But above all things, Erasistratus was interested in the heart and blood vessels. He described those membrane-thin formations in the heart, stretched out like a sail between auricle and ventricle, which Herophilus did not even mention. On the right side there were three, on the left two. They were just as transparent as the valves at the beginning of the aorta, but wider, and their free edge was drawn towards the wall of the heart by means of fine white threads.

Following the paths of the blood vessels, he made his way to the various organs, and when dissecting them he always found them filled with blood, just like the veins. Therefore, he thought,

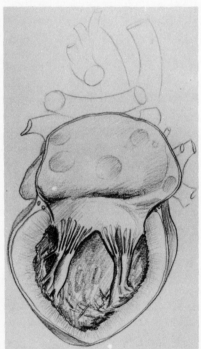

10. Valve inside the heart between auricle and ventricle first described by Erasistratus. (By S. Magyar)

the blood must have reached them through the veins. In the larger arteries, on the other hand, he found mostly air. From where else would the fresh air come, except from the lungs through the "vein-like arteries" (pulmonary veins) into the left side of the heart, whence the arteries conveyed it to every part of the body? Thus, he concluded, it had to be in the left ventricle that the inhaled air was transformed into an air-like substance maintaining life—the "life pneuma."

Sensation and movement, however, were conducted by the nerves, and Erasistratus believed that air reached the nervous system through the blood vessels of the brain, there to be transformed into a different kind of pneuma, which he called "soul pneuma." He assumed that this air was also in constant motion, starting from the brain and coursing through the body by means of the spinal cord and the nerves.

The coursing of the substances did not seem as uncertain to Erasistratus as the obscure theories concerning the discharge or accumulation of fluids. He detested generalizations. Moreover it was possible to demonstrate the exact location of the fluids. He now felt that he had a fairly clear picture of the whole. Three kinds of substances, he thought, made their way outward from the center: blood by way of the veins, "life pneuma" by way of the arteries, and "soul pneuma" by way of the nerves.

Yet how was it that while, after death, there was only a small amount of blood in the arteries besides air, when a live person received an injury, blood gushed out in profusion? Inside the heart, blood could not get through the partition dividing the two ventricles. And from the lungs nothing but air could come, as far as he was concerned. He could find just one possibility: that the blood permeated the limbs and organs through the veins into the arteries at invisible small spots.

Evidently the veins and arteries had to terminate in minute pores opening opposite each other, and which were normally closed. But if someone had fever, or ate and drank immoderately, thus producing more blood than necessary, then these "mouth-like endings" (anastomoses) would open and blood would flow from the veins into the empty arteries.

* * *

While Erasistratus experimented and lectured, bringing argu-

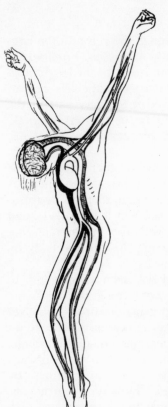

11. *The three substances according to Erasistratus. The blood in the veins is drawn black, the "life pneuma" in the arteries white, and the "soul pneuma" in the brain and nerves grey. (By A. Barabas)*

ment after argument to repudiate the theories of Herophilus, an Eastern Mediterranean power was gathering its forces against another older one. War broke out between Rome and Phoenician Carthage.

Now one side would gain the upper hand, now the other. The Carthaginians bribed the Sicilian cities, the Romans allied themselves with pirates. And while the Romans destroyed the Carthaginian fleet with their pirates, the Carthaginians swept over the Romans with their elephants and Numidian horsemen. The land power won a victory at sea, the sea power on land. But all this was only a beginning.

We do not know whether it was due to the uncertainties of

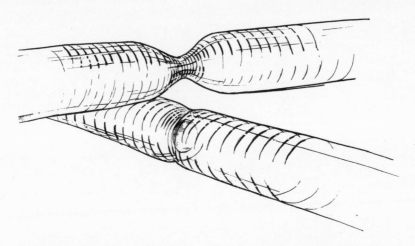

12. The "mouths" of veins and arteries opening into each other, ac-
cording to Erasistratus. Top: closed as in normal condition. Bottom:
as when disease is present. (by A. Barabas)

war, or to the changes following the death of his supporter, Ptolemy Philadelphus, in 247 B.C.; the fact is that Erasistratus left Alexandria and settled close to his homeland on the island of Samos. We have no knowledge of how long he lived there in retirement, far from the place of his successes. Records merely state that he became gravely ill. Most probably he tried valiantly to fight off the "accumulation of atoms," but in vain.

According to legend, when disease had tormented Erasistratus much too long he sighed: "Happy is the man who remembers his ancestors at the close of life."

He then prepared poison for himself and drank the contents of the cup.

CHAPTER TWO

GALEN IN ROME

■

Scarcely one year after the death of Ptolemy Philadelphus, war broke out between Egypt and Syria. The Egyptians were victorious and returned home laden with war loot. Among other things, they brought to Alexandria the papyrus scrolls taken from the library at Antioch. The catalogue of the Museum now listed 532,000 pieces.

Eratosthenes, the famous librarian, lectured to large audiences in the auditorium. Bold ideas were presented. The size of the earth, considered impossible to measure until then, was determined. Some time earlier Aristarchus had already estimated the relative diameter of the sun and the moon compared to that of the earth, but he had no idea of the earth's actual size. Eratosthenes, on the other hand, maintained that this could be calculated by means of a simple, logical deduction. Two points in the sky had to fall into a vertical continuation of two points on the earth. Therefore if the sky was pictured as a hemisphere spread over us (we only see as far as the horizon, the other half of the sphere being hidden by the earth itself), then the distance between the two points in the sky represents a small slice from a vast hemisphere spread above us. The size of this slice could be measured in proportion to the entire hemisphere. At the same time the two points reflected on the earth would be proportionate as well to the earth's hemisphere. Thus by means of a simple calculation the earth's size could be deduced. Eratosthenes may have only made an error of some fifty miles—a mere nothing when 25,000 are under discussion.

The fame of this and other investigations spread far and wide and stimulated the imagination of scientists and engineers. During this period, in Syracuse, Archimedes made a number of important discoveries. A few decades later Hipparchus calculated the distance between the moon and the earth with an error of scarcely one per cent.

All these contributions to science were achieved by Greek "philosophers." The Egyptians did not participate in elaborating these outstanding cosmological theories, which much later proved to have such a fundamental impact upon the changing of life on our globe. The constantly questioning, uncommitted way of thinking of the Greeks was not the way of the Egyptians.

There were other levels of estrangement, too. Egyptians resented the Greeks' near monopoly of high economic and governmental positions. Greeks collected the taxes and the sums gathered were not used for the welfare of the Egyptians.

And yet the Greeks had learned much from the Egyptians—even sculpture, and aspects of medical science, too. Homer himself had acknowledged in the *Odyssey*: "Everyone is a physician over there and their experience surpasses that of any man." Many Greeks, among them Pythagoras, Democritus and Plato, had spent some time in Egypt. They, the Egyptians, had been the teachers of the world, but now they merely served the usurping Greeks.

This was to last only a few decades longer, however, for time did not work for the conquerors. The Ptolemies slowly lost touch with Athens, and the further they drifted from the Greek way of life the more completely they were lost to Greek ways of thinking.

Certain external features were still reminiscent of the old country: the theatres, chariot races and the Olympic games; but these were mere echoes. The Pharaoh ruled unapproachably from Amon Ra's earthly throne, and it was virtually impossible for an ordinary mortal to reach his presence. The ideals of unrestricted research and criticism were forgotten. The Pharoah did not care to risk being judged by any philosopher.

Before long the Museum scholars no longer received salaries, and they were dismissed. This action was rectified later, but measures of this kind tended to dampen their original enthusiasm, and their former zest was never recaptured.

The Ptolemaic dynasty began to lose the military superiority held by its first members. Not forty years after their Syrian victory the Pharaohs, and with them Egypt, found themselves in a position subordinate to Rome, now strengthened by the success of the Punic wars.

❊ ❊ ❊

After the defeat of Hannibal in 201 B.C. Rome proved invincible. She swept over her enemies one after the other: she conquered the Macedons in 168 B.C., destroyed Corinth in 133 B.C., defeated the King of Numidia in 106 B.C., the rebellious Teutonic tribes in 102 B.C., and forced the retreat of the King of Pontus in 72 B.C. The ships laden with Spanish silver and Syrian silks now docked at Rome's harbor of Ostia. And Alexandria's glitter began to fade.

After defeating external and internal enemies, the leaders of Rome set about establishing the foundations of their own personal power. When hostilities broke out between Pompeius and Caesar it was the quicker, the younger, the bolder who prevailed. Caesar defeated the armies of Pompeius in 48 B.C.

Pompeius managed with the greatest difficulty to escape to Egypt. It was a great honor for the Egyptian Pharaoh that the most distinguished of the Optimates should seek refuge with him, but it was by no means very comfortable. For what could be expected now? Obviously that Caesar would enter Alexandria and turn it into a battle field.

The 17-year old Dionysius, the twelfth Pharaoh of the Ptolemaic dynasty, took the advice of his counselors and had Pompeius killed. They thought that now they had nothing to fear from Caesar, as far as Egyptian territory was concerned. Unfortunately, Caesar, completely ignorant of these happenings, was already at sea. He was en route to Alexandria to strike a blow at Pompeius and to make his victory complete. When he reached the harbor he immediately made his way to the Pharaoh's palace. The Pharaoh and his court tried to placate him by proffering the head of Pompeius, but at the same time it was plain that they were not pleased to see him. They used every means at their disposal to make Caesar's stay as disagreeable as possible.

To strengthen his position, Caesar formed an alliance with Cleopatra, the sister-wife of Pharaoh Dionysius. Cleopatra was not in favor with the young pharaoh; he, because of her complicity with Caesar, was enraged to the point of threatening war. He pretended to be calmed by Caesar's words of conciliation, and agreed to abide by his late father's injunction that he and Cleopatra should rule their country jointly. Secretly, however, Dionysius went ahead with his plans, and on the occasion of what was to have been a peace banquet succeeded in isolating the major portion of Caesar's forces in the royal palace.

When this was known to him Caesar ordered the harbor set on fire. The huts on the docks collapsed one after the other. The wind blew in from the sea, the flames veered towards the city. The fire encroached further and further in, reaching the Palace and the buildings surrounding it. It reached the pavilions of the Museum and finally the Library. The dry papyrus scrolls, many of them impregnated with cedar oil against insects, caught fire. Within a few hours all the scrolls, which by this time numbered some 900,000 were burned to ashes.

Caesar himself only escaped with his life by swimming away from the hail of arrows aimed at him from the Egyptian ships in the harbor. After much warfare he finally achieved victory. The young Pharaoh disappeared on the field of battle without a trace, his armies were scattered; Cleopatra was left sole ruler in the ancient land of Egypt (46 B.C.).

And now the world conqueror and brilliant orator, the cold-blooded adventurer, cynically lavish with other people's money, the ever alert, disciplined work-machine finally allowed himself the luxury of a holiday. For the first time in decades he took a rest, spending several months more or less alone with Cleopatra.

He was finally roused by the news of trouble further east, and going there with the utmost speed he was once again victorious. After defeating the remainder of Pompeius' supporters he returned to Rome to organize the state according to his own ideas. He had work started on a number of new buildings and had the discarded statues of Pompeius put back in their places. He settled wild bands of soldiers in cultivated areas, had the mud dredged out of the harbor at Ostia, and made a calendar.

Nor did he forget the tragedy of the loss of the Museum at Alexandria. It even occurred to him that he might transfer the seat of his empire to Alexandria, for which idea obviously Cleopatra must have been in some measure responsible. But he soon dismissed the temptation. What would the Romans have said!

In his state he assigned a more important role to his scholars than any ruler before him. And to emphasize this, he gave rights of citizenship to the teachers of the "free sciences" and to physicians. Also, plans were under discussion for a huge library. He entrusted the task to Terentius Varro.

Varro was a man of enormous learning. Three hundred years later, St. Augustine was still puzzled as to how he had had the time to read all the works he described, when a whole lifetime would scarcely have been sufficient to have skimmed through them. In his encyclopedia there was information concerning agriculture, stock-breeding and medicine. He was the first to describe the minute "creatures" invisible to the naked eye, present in the air, which when inhaled could cause serious infectious diseases. True, he lacked proof, but experience bore him out. And breaking with tradition, Varro included medicine in the "Nine books of Science."

Without doubt he was the man best qualified to create the new center of scholarship, provided Caesar contributed what was necessary. And with his broad outlook, great culture, powers of organization, the new institute should indeed have surpassed its Alexandrian model. But the Ides of March intervened, and Caesar died (44 B.C.).

His enemies soon discovered what they had lost in him, but in vain did Brutus, tormented by his conscience, keep saying: "It would have been better not to kill Caesar." They could not bring him back to life, and no one else carried out those plans of his which might have led Rome along an entirely different road.

After his death Rome was once more plunged into the turmoil of civil war from which Caesar's nephew Octavian eventually emerged triumphant. He took the title of Augustus, and the Republic became an Empire (31 B.C.).

Augustus was neither the best nor the worst of Roman emperors. He had roads constructed, palaces and temples built, provided security for the citizenry, at the same time allowing them, although watching them closely, to defy him. He encouraged writers and poets, but like most Romans had only a remote respect for the natural sciences. The Romans considered it beneath their dignity to work with their hands, and thus their chief contribution to the natural sciences was to collect knowledge amassed by Greeks and others. Experimentation, anything that involved the use of instruments, was considered suitable occupation only for slaves or foreigners.

* * *

After the death of Varro, Pliny the Elder undertook the task of compiling a more modern scientific encyclopedia than did Varro. Pliny's was a collection of the writings of some two thousand Greek authors; but it contained no new material.

The only comprehensive work of the time on medicine was that of Celsus, a patrician layman. A clever writer, he wrote a pleasant work, it being an interesting kind of venture in a field not very well known to him. But the writings of Celsus are merely accidental exceptions, written to occupy a nobleman's ennui. There is nothing like them in a thousand years of Roman history. Moreover, he wrote in Greek instead of Latin. It was no exaggeration on the part of Cato when he said: "We conquered and were conquered." The language of science remained Greek and the empire, serving as a model with its postal service, communications and canal construction, did not possess any sort of advanced school for the teaching of medical science.

Those slaves living in Rome, freed Greeks and Syrians, or others who wished to become physicians, became appreticed to surgeons, or sometimes charlatans. The distinctions between the conjuring magician and the serious physician became vague in

this city, where that "Master of the best things," as Pliny had
called old Cato, still found ready listeners when he prescribed
kohlrabi against headaches, deafness—and adenoids. In the
country the doctor prescribed an amulet made of jasper against
stomach ache, particularly effective if accompanied by mystical
murmurings such as: "Huat, hauat, ista, pista, sista, dannabo,
dannaustra."

Medical knowledge was not based on any common fundamen-
tals, state examinations, oath of office, or time spent on study.
Some doctors openly claimed they could make a first-rate physician within one year (for a fee of course) out of anyone who
applied. Drugs, diverse and exotic, were advertised for the same
ailment by physicians living side by side, whether they had
their offices in the smart quarters of the Quirinal or Viminal or
in the grimy houses of Subura.

Some Roman doctors made money not only from the practice
of medicine. If there was no market for their drugs or poison
powders and if all else failed, there was always a job to be
had as grave digger. According to the fashionable poet Martialis, there was not too much difference in any case between a
grave digger and a doctor.

These facts were not unknown to the young Greeks aspiring
to a career in medicine. If they wanted to become real physicians Rome, with its hundreds of temples, thousands of palaces and all of its money, could not give them the means. They
made a pilgrimage to Athens or Alexandria where the library
of the Serapion was still standing, even though the Museum had
been burned down. But this was a different Alexandria from
that of the days of Erasistratus. Four hundred years had passed
since then, and the desire for personal experimentation was no
longer so strong in scientists. In the atmosphere of suspicion
and accusation which accompanies political upheaval only those
could get ahead who were themselves suspicious and who made
accusations in self-defence. And since science can only be advanced by very sincere persons willing to fly boldly in the face
of other people's opinions, such people were bound to meet
their downfall rather promptly in their struggle with the un-
derhanded. Only those could maintain their positions who could
hide behind an illustrious name and find protection in the protection of its fame.

There developed the habit of quoting the Ancients, the practice of slavishly following celebrities, since this was convenient and not at all dangerous. The students of the pupils of Erasistratus believed in him as in a god, forgetting that he himself had not listened to other men, or learned from books, but only from that "great artist, Nature." Dissection was still practised, but merely in imitation, without independent thought and much to the disapproval of the so-called Empirics. These held that life processes and the symptoms of disease could only be learned from observation at the bedside of the patient; for dissection, particularly live dissection, changed the existing situation. Anyone performing live dissection—even though only on animals—was no better than a butcher, they said.

The Methodists, followers of Asclepiades, the once-fashionable Roman practitioner, were of the same opinion, and attributed disease, death, and recovery to the pores of the skin. Asclepiades himself mercilessly attacked Erasistratus for assuming the presence of valves of some kind in the heart, where Herophilus, who had done so much dissecting, did not even mention them.

At length one man appeared who was not taken in by the Dogmatists or the Empirics or the Methodists. He was a Greek from Pergamum, the small Near Eastern kingdom under Roman influence. His father did not want him to inherit his mother's argumentative, scolding nature, and to this end he even tried to influence his son's character by naming him "Peaceful One", or Galen.

Galen had spent long years studying in Smyrna and Corinth. His industry was unequalled, his memory infallible, his powers of observation alert and accurate. He flaunted his knowledge with such sweeping self-assurance, quotations falling from his mouth in such an abundant stream that even the professors were uneasy when lecturing in his presence. Hardly a "peaceful one", he formed opinions instantly, knew only yes or no, and ruthlessly snubbed those who contradicted him. He did not know hesitation. In his conceit he felt, particularly after visiting Alexandria, that he was qualified to judge any aspect of medical science, or any of its personalities.

In Pergamum, where his father was a distinguished architect and rich citizen held in high regard, Galen's practice started out with a flourish of success. At first, slaves, snake charmers and athletes consulted him. He was a clever surgeon and careful in his prescriptions, so the number of his patients grew, especially since he used his learning and origins shrewdly to his advantage. He could talk with equal ease the language of simple people and that of the philosophers. Soon patients began to arrive from neighboring villages and islands, undertaking the fatigues of the sea journey solely on his account.

For the summer sports season he was appointed physician for the gladiators. He set the sprains suffered by the wrestlers, bandaged the cuts suffered in equestrian contests. He gave attention to the prevention of infection by washing out the wounds with red wine, which owing to its alcoholic content acted as an antiseptic. He bandaged fractures more tightly than had been usual. In that first year no one died of injuries, which was a great achievement; none of his predecessors had had such excellent results. He began to be talked about. He was reappointed without demur and held this position for four years in Pergamum.

But here on the edge of the empire he could at best become a local celebrity. For wide-spread fame and real financial success it was necessary to go to the capital.

Galen was thirty-three when he moved to Rome (around 160 A.D.). Until then he had been surrounded by friendly faces. Much as he had despised the athletes, he had to admit that there had been peace, understanding, and humane chivalry, even in the arenas and sporting grounds in Greece. But in Rome!

The noise in the streets was deafening. Street vendors offered their wares with tremendous shouts, from the schoolhouses the monotonous murmur of children at their lessons could be heard, then the hammering of artisans and the hoarse scraping of saws, all unceasingly. At dawn he heard the squeaking of the vegetable vendors' carts, in the afternoons two hundred and fifty thousand throats yelled "blue, blue" or "green, green", in encouragement to their favorite chariot drivers in the Circus Maximus. Further away from the Palatine, just below the Esquiline Hill, in the Flavian amphitheatre, people would be sweating in the sweltering heat, their eyes fixed on the arena underneath the brick-red canvas awning. The fight here was to the death. Thracian and Gallic gladiators would pursue each other with a dagger in one hand and a net in the other. They would yell roughly at each other: "It's not you I want to catch —I want to catch a fish. Why do you flee, O Gaul?" But if one succeeded in throwing the net over his adversary, the dagger did not remain idle for long. Later the air would be rent by the growling of bears from the Alps and the roar of Nubian lions. Murderers, rebellious slaves or Christians stood pale and trembling, awaiting death.

Life in Rome for a Greek spectator seemed rough and uninhibited, unrestrained and undisciplined; even art was only borrowed. What they built according to their own conceptions, such as the Pantheon, was clumsy and ungainly compared to the Temple of Zeus in Pergamum, or any other public building there. And to crown everything, their entire culture was Greek, although they liked to deceive themselves into believing that Rome was at the summit of everything.

His colleagues, Galen found, were repulsive, avaricious, malicious and worst of all, ignorant. Indeed, he found little to like in Rome, but if he wished for success he had to embark upon his practice there without delay.

He was in luck. An old philosopher from Pergamum, a friend of his father's, invited him to treat his undulating fever. Galen predicted when the fever would cease. The old man was dumbfounded and told everyone that "Apollo spoke through the mouth of Galen." He was cured exactly on the day predicted. The cure itself was not considered as astounding as Galen's ability to see into the future. He was thought to possess magic powers, like the Babylonian astrologers or the Sibyl of Delphi.

Galen's name began to be mentioned in distinguished circles. At first, as a precautionary measure, a slave would be sent to test the abilities of this wonder doctor from Pergamum. After a short while patricians and former consuls began to come to him for advice. His friends persuaded him to hold public lectures on breathing and the origins of the voice.

Opposite the Forum, in the colonnaded hall of the Temple of Vespasian, they set up a hollow wooden bench shaped like a trough, to which they tied a pig. A crowd of dignitaries, jaded

by too many chariot races and gladiators, were present, seeking new excitement.

They saw Galen set the spinal cord free, making the nerve roots
visible. The thorax of the animal shook with convulsions and
it exhaled air with a gasp. Galen cut through the spinal cord
at the level of the sixth thoracic vertebra. The squealing sub-
sided, now only the diaphragm heaved at intervals, and the
intercostal muscles were largely paralyzed. He then cut through
the cord further up, at the level of the fourth cervicle vertebra,
whereupon the animal became entirely silent. Breathing stopped,
for breathing is conducted through the spinal cord and nerves
transmitting the will from the brain to the breathing muscles.

Shorthand writers took down all they heard. Galen talked,
words poured from him without restraint. He was in his element: turning ingratiatingly towards his audience he abused the
Sophists, assuring the listeners that their "healthy understanding" was far superior to the Sophists' false knowledge. The audience was duly impressed. A man who would dare to say such
things as "Who before me would have been capable of grasping
this wonderful natural phenomenon?", and who openly called
the great Erasistratus simple-minded, *had* to be really very
clever.

Unfortunately, there were colleagues present also. The rivals,
with their assured positions, some of them court physicians,
could scarcely be expected to endure with equanimity the sight
of this recently arrived stranger from a distant province taking
all the honors and later, assuredly, the fees as well. They
heckled him, making remarks calculated to throw a false light
on what he had been saying. If this was not successful they re-
sorted to slander—at one point Galen was even afraid of being
poisoned. When he had been in Rome barely a year he was
forced to the decision not to perform in public any more, and
to talk even less in private houses.

But he had another way to show his greatness—through writing.
While still in Pergamum he had completed manuscripts on Aristotle and Plato and a few commentaries upon the Hippocratic
teachings. In Rome he started out to check the confused data
put forth by the hostile methodists, pneumatists, empirics and
other medical sectarians.

At first he but dissected pigs, goats and dogs; later he received bears from the amphitheatre; then fish, birds and snakes—any creature that was available. The most valuable, of course, was the monkey, since it resembled man most closely. In the course of his whole life he only dissected two human bodies: an already somewhat decomposed corpse fished out of the water, and the remains of an executed man, as much as was left upon the scaffold by the vultures. Thus it was animals, chiefly monkeys, that served as his guides in his researches into the composition of the body.

Knife and forceps were at work indefatigably, whether the body was dead or alive and moving. He wanted to learn the purpose of Nature. He wrote: "True faith does not manifest itself in hecatombic sacrifices or fragrant incense burning, but in the knowledge and spreading of wisdom."

Cutting into the living flesh, it happened sometimes that he severed an artery. Blood poured from it, gushing out rhythmically with every pulse beat, every time the heart contracted. There was no time for the "synanastomoses" to open, as Erasistratus had taught, to allow the passage of blood from the veins. This meant that the blood was already in the arteries.

Was it possible that the heart sent blood to every part of the body by way of the arteries and not only air, as Erasistratus had taught? If so, the pulse beats should cease if the artery was bound. And that is in fact what happened. But this did not satisfy Galen. What happened when he loosened the bandage? The pulse beats were resumed, therefore they had to originate from the heart.

But Galen still found this insufficient proof. He carefully surrounded an artery, taking pains not to injure the wall of the blood vessel. A long stretch of the narrow tube lay before him, expanding and collapsing rhythmically. But supposing it did contain pneuma and that blood only entered from the veins once the blood vessel was damaged?

He tied down the artery at two points and opened it: blood ran out of it, but there was no trace of air. Yet if the blood had entered by way of Erasistratus's holes from the veins, the blood could only have entered through the binding situated furthest from the heart. If, on the other hand, it came from the heart

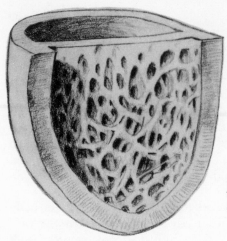

13. *Partition between the two ventricles showing numerous deep ridges. (By A. Barabas)*

itself, then it would continue to flow once the binding closest to the heart was loosened.

He took a goose feather, cut off the ends to form a tube. He stuck it into the blood vessel so that one end was directed towards the heart, while the other hung out unconnected. When the binding was loosened the wave of pulsation started out from the heart and the blood splashed out through the free end of the goose feather. If, on the other hand, the blood vessel was tied down at the inside end, pulsation ceased and the blood stopped flowing out of the open end.

There was no question about it: there was blood in the arteries and not air, and it was pushed into them by the left ventricle. This much was certain.

Unfortunately, this only served to complicate the explanation of the flow of blood as well as that of the pneuma. For an airlike substance, pneuma, was thought to be pouring from the lungs into the left auricle and ventricle, and not blood. But where did the pneuma go from there? And how did blood, in spite of all this reasoning, get into the left ventricle?

There was no other way except from the right ventricle, Galen thought. There was, to be sure, a thick muscular partition between the two, but there were fairly deep ridges and holes on its surface which he thought must lead from the right to the left ventricle by means of invisibly small connections.

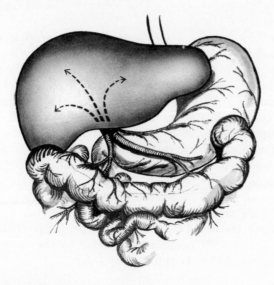

14. *Blood vessels spreading from the stomach and intestines to the liver. (By A. Barabas)*

The renewal of the blood had to take place in the left ventricle, since there Galen found it to be bright red, while in the right ventricle and in the veins it was dark. What made the blood so light colored in the left ventricle? Obviously, the pneuma absorbed by the blood vessels connecting the lungs with the left auricle.

Gradually he thought he was beginning to see how the blood streamed in every direction. It seemed quite clear to him. According to Galen, the blood, filled with nutrition from the stomach and the intestines, coursed towards the liver.

In the liver the blood was digested, took on a different form, was purified. From there it went out through the veins as "physical pneuma" into every part of the body and the heart; that is, into the right ventricle.

This was the blood which provided the body with nutrition. The other part, drawn into the right ventricle was just as dark, being full of "soot." The heart function sent a fraction of it from there into the lungs, partly to give the lungs nutrition, just like all the other organs, and partly to rid the body of the unclean part by ejecting it by means of the lungs. Another part of the blood again flowed into the left ventricle through the supposed holes in the partition dividing the two ventricles.

The blood entering the left ventricle combined with the pneuma which the heart drew from the lungs through the small branches of the trachea via the vein-like arteries and the left auricle. In the left ventricle, according to Galen, the color of the blood, dark blue up to this point, changed and became bright red. This indicated that a significant change had occurred: "Life pneuma" had been produced, carrying, not nourishment, but life into the various organs by way of the intricate branches of the arteries.

From the aorta the blood could not get back into the left ventricle, being prevented by the valves situated at its starting point. Similarly the blood flowing towards the lungs could never get back into the right ventricle, prevented by the valves at the root of the artery-like vein (pulmonary artery).

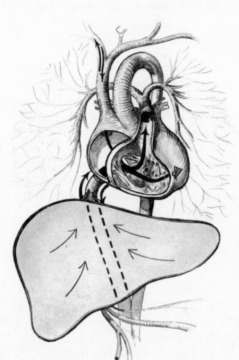

15. Blood streaming from the liver into the veins and heart. (By A. Barabas)

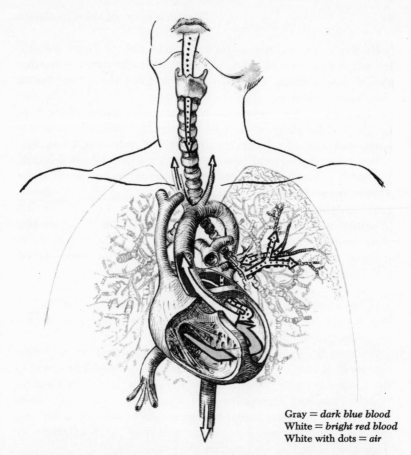

Gray = *dark blue blood*
White = *bright red blood*
White with dots = *air*

16. Blood seeping from the right ventricle into the left, air streaming from the lungs to the same place and their unification in the left ventricle resulting in red blood or "life pneuma" distributed through the arteries, as thought by Galen. (By A. Barabas)

In the eleventh chapter of his work on the "Function of Organs" Galen writes: "All these things, and particularly the general purpose of the valves, is to prevent a reversal of flow of any sort. . . . For Nature does not want to tire the heart with unnecessary work, nor commit the error of putting anything at a place from which she intends to take it away again, or lead it away from a place where its presence is necessary."

He wrote further that in the transmission of the blood, breathing plays an important part. Not only does the pressure exerted by exhalation cause the outward flow from the heart, but it also closes the valves.

"Apart from these functions, breathing also affects blood flow, for the combination of air entering the left ventricle from the lungs and the blood flowing into it from the right ventricle create heat which could become dangerous if not cooled by air.

"The red blood, this purified life-giving substance, is of course lighter than the dark 'sooty' substance in the right ventricle. And that this is so is shown by the fact that the left ventricle is naturally thicker, so the sooty, heavier half on the other side of the heart should not cause imbalance."

Galen was convinced he had left no question unanswered. Everything seemed so clear and easy to understand.

* * *

Galen wrote and uttered a disdainful remarks about his "stupid, impertinent and ignorant" Roman colleagues—which proved very advantageous in building up his practice.

Students began to gather round him and his patients no longer consisted merely of patricians and retired consuls. The uncle of the Emperor Verus came, and the son-in-law of the co-Emperor Marcus Aurelius. This young man was so completely captivated by Galen's self-assurance and personality that he asked his father-in-law to allow the miracle maker to hold a lecture on these new, incredible and irrefutable discoveries.

Marcus Aurelius gave permission for the lecture; preparations were started in spite of a somewhat uneasy feeling in the city. There were vague rumors about some ghastly disease brought back by the soldiers returning from the Parthian wars; and more and more people took to their beds, never to rise again.

At this point Galen had an open road into the Emperor's palace. Perhaps even he had not expected such a meteoric rise as this when he had arrived in Rome four years previously.

Yet the new epidemic could destroy his fame in a few weeks. Galen was cautious: his existence in Rome could survive only if his drugs would prove to be successful. If the results were in doubt he was never impatient, but rather waited, or withdrew. He knew very well that he was helpless in the face of this epidemic. In order to win time he asked that *he* might be allowed to set the date for his lecture.

Meanwhile, his slave made contact with a suburban agent and turned his personal effects into cash. Without taking leave of his friends Galen travelled to the sea port of Brundisium to board the first ship sailing to Pergamum, his home city (166 A.D.).

Meanwhile the Emperor Verus returned from the Near East with the bulk of his troops and the epidemic broke out with unbridled force.

Peace had to be made promptly with the Parthians, but the Marcomanni, a Germanic tribe which settled in Central Europe, took advantage of Rome's moment of weakness and attacked from the north.

The recruitment of fresh troops progressed very slowly. Members of distinguished families fled to the Sabine Hills or to their villas in Campania, while the village people kept out of sight. Everyone was in the grip of the fear of death. The epidemic continued to rage in Rome. In the poor quarters of Subura, in the crowded quarters of the five or six-storied tenements where Galen's agent lived, people died by the hundred every day. And as the weeks went by the number grew to four or five thousand.

Marcus Aurelius and Verus traveled to Italy proper to inspect their departing troops. Dejected as they were, they felt that Galen might be able to help and therefore sent a courier for him. He kept postponing his return and in fact succeeded in winning several months, but finally had to leave Pergamum. Even so, his journey somehow took much longer than the homeward trip had done. He even left his books behind in Pergamum hoping that he would find some excuse to turn back. But the imperial command left no room for escape any longer: he had to obey.

Hè arrived in Aquileia where the epidemic was at its worst. The two Emperors fled to Rome (perhaps upon his advice), but one of them, Verus, died on the way.

In spite of these misfortunes, the war could no longer be postponed. The Marcomanni had already penetrated deep into the territory of the Empire. Marcus Aurelius made his preparations

without further delay. He wanted to take Galen along with him,
but the latter produced one excuse after the other. His persistent reluctance proved successful. He knew the Emperor and
knew that he could overcome the "Ruler of the World." In
his "Confessions" Marcus Aurelius wrote: "We were born to work
together . . . like a pair of legs, hands, eyes, like an upper
and lower row of teeth. Therefore to work against each other
would be against Nature."

The Emperor gave in. Galen was allowed to travel with the
Emperor's small son in areas far away from the danger zones,
but obviously his object was not the one professed, that of
"avoiding the usual ill-will of the other doctors."

Once again he was lucky. The boy, Commodus, became fever-
ish. Galen examined the child and diagnosed tonsillitis. His judgment proved correct once more and by the third day the child
had no more fever.

Galen was finally master of the situation. Now he scarcely
had to fear the malice and ire of his city rivals.

If one of the sectarians of inferior intellect got into a discussion with him concerning blood flow he informed them that all
they had to do was to read his book "The Function of Various
Organs". Where did the blood disappear to in the tissues? It
was used up, and what little was required as replacement was
prepared by the liver.

And just as the "spiritus naturalis" contained in the dark blue
blood coursed from the liver through the veins into every part
of the body, so the heart sent out the "spiritus vitalis" contained
in the bright red blood by way of the arteries.

For the heart worked without ceasing. If it were removed from
a living animal and placed on a table, it went on beating for
quite a long time, then more and more infrequently, stopping entirely for a while, only to contract a few more times.
For a long time after the ventricles ceased to move, the right
auricle would continue to beat.

Galen had observed all this; but gradually, as his fame grew,
he lost the time he needed for animal experiments. Not only
did he attend the inhabitants of the Palatine, or treat the hys-
terical headaches of some woman who had developed an
attachment for the star of the amphitheatre's dancing group, not

only did he have to listen to the complaint of members of the imperial family; but imploring letters came from Spain, Gaul, Asia Minor, begging the wonder doctor to cure their ills with his skills. And Galen eagerly responded to them all.

He owed his success not only to his comprehensive knowledge and practical experience. For his power to inspire faith created a precarious, shadowy edifice, erected by himself; similarly with the secrets which only he knew of, so that, remarkable stage director that he was, he even managed to deceive the other doctors.

When he entered the sick room, he pretended to examine the pulse with absorbed concentration, while his gaze wandered over the furnishings. Soon, with a few questions, he started a flow of talk from his apprehensive patient. Like a master detective, within a matter of minutes he formed an opinion concerning the patient's emotional state, circumstances and habits. He then proceeded to make remarks so appropriate as to amaze the assembled friends and relations. He really was a miracle doctor—they thought. All this he learned just from the pulse!

For days on end he would have no opportunity to write, he was fashionable, he was a success. When the chief court physician died, Marcus Aurelius appointed him successor.

The war with the Germanic tribes went on for years; and duty required the Emperor to remain with his troops. When at last the war ended (176 A.D.) he returned to Rome. After Galen had cured a complaint of his, the Emperor charged him with the production of daily doses of antidotes for poisons. Galen had to concoct potions made from ingredients imported at great expense from Egypt, India and Britanny. The Emperor trusted him and called him first among the physicians and the only one among the philosophers.

The peace, however, did not last long. Marcus Aurelius had to go into battle again, but this time took his son the now grown Commodus, with him. The future ruler had to know something of war, to excel in all things and particularly to know thoroughly the men of the legions.

The old warlike virtues had not remained intact among the Romans and, forced by necessity, the Emperor had even had to tolerate Christians among his troops. At home he would have had them executed in the interests of the Empire, but on the field of battle he had to pretend ignorance for, curiously, these men were models of discipline and obedience.

Epidemics flared up from time to time and cruelly decimated the ranks of the divisions. The Emperor himself fell ill. He sent for Commodus, handed over to him the leadership of his armies, then dismissed him from his tent so as not to pass the disease on to his beloved son.

* * *

After his father's death (A.D. 181) Commodus returned to Rome. He did not think much of the carefully selected civil servants and senators and soon dismissed them all. He put a stop to visits from Galen, claiming he had no use for magic potions.

Cast aside, Galen pursued his practice and scientific work. Books on fever, pulse, and the art of healing appeared by his hand one after the other. He did not keep the manuscripts at home. In such an uncertain world, one never knew. . . . He took them to a room in the Temple of Peace to be guarded by the priests.

Unfortunately, the Temple caught fire one day. The fire guard which had functioned so admirably in the old days, should have been called. But the incumbents of the city posts, including officials of the fire brigade, appointed on the basis of momentary favor, were not masters of the situation. They were afraid to say anything, to do anything, let alone to give orders. People by the thousands were already being executed or imprisoned as a result of the smallest complaint or protest.

The burning temple was completely consumed by the flames. Some books of Galen's were destroyed forever. Most, however, survived, for the papyrus scroll merchants had had the greater part of them copied.

There seemed no end to Commodus' reign of terror. And what made it more sinister was that he was now no longer content with the excitements of the amphitheatre. A favorite joke of his, for instance, was to order someone to the palace with the message that the Emperor himself would condescend to shave him and, as the deathly pale face blinked timidly under the foam, to cut off—by accident of course—an ear or a nose. The mixture of red blood and white shaving soap provoked screams of joy and excitement. Another equally interesting spectacle was that of watching the Emperor operate. The patient was tied down and the emperor chopped off arms and legs with his own imperial hands. What need was there of Galen, when the emperor himself was the best of surgeons?

The courtiers fawned, inwardly terrified, and slept badly, for time and again Commodus had had his most intimate favorite executed, and then his successor. Who could expect mercy in such circumstances?

Finally, when his wife found her own name at the head of a list of intended victims for the next execution, she acted quickly. She mixed poison in his drink, and to be sure there was no possibility of his survival she arranged for a gladiator to be on hand to strangle him as soon as the poison began to take effect (A.D.193).

* * *

In Commodus' thirteen-year reign the moral standards of the civil servants had deteriorated and the soldiery had become depraved. After a period of chaos Septimius Severus gained control and imposed a regimen of rigid discipline.

Galen re-emerged, and once again he made visits to the new Emperor's palace. But how the atmosphere had changed since the days of Marcus Aurelius! They were now not content merely to be cured by him: the Emperor's wife decided she was entitled to have her beauty preparations made up by her physician. A vain woman, she was unable to endure the thought that the hair style represented in her statue might seem old fashioned after a few years. The court hairdresser, therefore, had to make one new wig after the other for the statue, as the fashion in hair styles changed. Naturally, her friends did not wish to be left out of such a trend. As for Galen, he meant no more and no less to them than any one of the servants charged with obtaining their cosmetics.

Without enthusiasm, he gave instructions about how to make black hair golden, what paints should be used to etch the outlines of the eyebrows, and he gave advice concerning the perspiration of the hands. He even had to concoct perfumes.

Yet his experiences in the field of cosmetics gave him an insight into new territories in his study of the human body and out of this knowledge, acquired much against his will, he was able to derive some benefit as a scientist. He incorporated this knowledge into his work on pharmacology.

There thus remained no aspect of the living body concerning which he had not expressed his opinion. He gave entirely new, individual and useful instructions about everything affecting health and disease, and he felt that he had succeeded in smoothing out the rugged paths of ancient medical science, just as "Trajan had done it with the roads to war." No question remained unanswered, no problem remained obscure. Hesitation and doubt never disturbed the assurance of his writing. There could be no mistakes in his diagnoses and treatments. He was the Great Galen, the "Peaceful One."

In the works of Hippocrates we not infrequently find the humble admission that he had erred. But Galen's medical histories read like a series of triumphant marches against the stupidity of others. What he writes, based on the experiments and experiences of many years, together with "wisdom received from Asclepius", pretends to be all-clear, plausible and logical. Where were those who had attacked him in his young days? And what had become of the atoms of the methodists and of the all-powerful pores?

In the whole of Galen's teaching there was perfect order, just as there was in the State under Septimius Severus, and it seemed then that this order could never again be disrupted.

When he died (201 A.D.), no one would have dared to cast any doubt upon his verbal legacy: "Anyone who, like me, aspires to become famous for his deeds rather than for pompous speeches, must relentlessly absorb everything which I have stated after a lifetime of hard-working research."

CHAPTER THREE

FROM CAIRO TO SICILY TO FLORENCE

■

The great epidemic which started in Galen's time raged for almost twenty years. It took at least ten million lives in the Roman Empire. Never before had the "Senate and the Roman People" suffered such a crushing loss—and caused by invisible and all-pervading pathogenes. Large numbers from the legions and many of the commanders died; in the cities, where the epidemic was at its worst, tens of thousands of proconsuls, officials, merchants and soldiers succumbed within a few years. The barbarians, on the other hand, in their scattered villages and tents, avoided most of the danger.

Everything which made the life of the Roman citizenry secure and envied—the administration, the carefully developed practices of law, maintenance of waterways and roads—slipped into the hands of men of foreign culture and tongues. It was during this period that the foreign legions and foreign commanders first appeared in the history of Rome; and no more than twenty years after the death of Galen a non-Roman, a Thracian shepherd boy, became Emperor (Maximinus Thrax).

In another great empire, that of China, the reigning dynasty collapsed at the same time and for the same reason, splitting the country into two. Just as in China, the flood of migrating nations appeared on the frontiers of the Roman Empire at a moment of weakness, a flood which could only have been withstood by the most strenuous effort of a determined and vigorous nation. It was not one people which hammered at the doors, not one single army, which might have been defeated or destroyed, or with which peace might have been made. No sooner had one wave been pushed back than the next one came from some other direction with new tactics, barbaric cunning and ferocity. Rome was unable, just as China and India had been, to withstand and cope with such unleashed nomadic forces. In vain did the Emperor Hadrian (117-138 A.D.) build belts of fortifications at the most vulnerable points of the Empire, between the sources of the Rhine and the Danube. In vain did the Emperor Aurelianus reinforce Rome itself with enormous fortress walls (270-75 A.D.). He could not stop the ever-increasing and ever-changing pressure of the barbarians. For a while Rome maintained her position; but then she started for certain on the downward path.

Seventy years after the death of Marcus Aurelius the Goths defeated the legions, killed the Emperor Decius (251 A.D.) and broke through the Danubian frontier. It was the end of Rome's five hundred years of peace from external enemies. Not long afterwards, Alaric's Visigoths were seen in the streets of Rome (410 A.D.), setting fire to palaces, robbing, pillaging, raping. They represented but the first humiliation. Attila's Huns later destroyed seventy flourishing Roman cities, and they still were better than their followers, the Vandals. Obviously, it was impossible for creative thought and calm debate to flourish in such an atmosphere, when daily bread and the defense of life itself required undivided effort.

After some centuries of bloody chaos these surging, wandering peoples began to congregate at certain points where they eventually settled. They began to exchange tents for houses built of stone and upon becoming acquainted with Roman machines of war, with the paved roads of their cities, the harp, papyrus scrolls, they learned about the gods of the Empire as well: about Jupiter, Mithras, Isis—and Jesus.

As time went on the religion of Christ, spreading and strength-
ening, began to eclipse the others. This creed did not proclaim
a fearful and oppressive God; on the contrary, it presented
to men an uplifting awareness of a conscience within themselves and the importance of their individual opinions. It promised not only happiness after death, but just and equal treatment from a higher power, full rights of citizenship in the Kingdom of Heaven for the slave just as for the patrician. Everything
which might lead to an improvement in their circumstances, a
more humane life, and more exalted consciousness, was promised those who followed the road of true Christianity.

To make the religion more universally accepted, however, was
not easy. Incessant vigilance, heroism required at times when
events took an unexpected turn, sword wielding—these were the
virtues of those days. Science, philosophical discussion, argument, the written word, had become not only superfluous, but
dangerous. So much so that in order to be rid of the "demoraliz-
ing" effects of the ancient scholars, a local official of the Emperor
Theodosius ordered the branch library of the Alexandrian Museum, the Serapeum, set afire (389 A.D.). Thereby Alexandria's
leading position in scientific life was over for good.

It took nearly five hundred years (400-900 A.D.) for the tribes
invading Rome's European possessions to finally settle and to
outstrip or overgrow the decaying remains of the Roman Empire. In turn the Crusades, which began in 1096 A.D., brought
about a new meeting of East and West. Europeans learned,
though rarely on the highest of levels, about new people, new
countries, different ideas. Merchants discovered that blades from
Damascus were profitable to sell, even if made by Moslems;
and that spices flavored dull meats even if they came from distant places where Christ's name was unknown. Cultures of
Africa and Asia, often older, richer and more illustrious than
anything in Europe, aroused and lured.

* * *

The trade routes, when they left the territory of Christendom,
led through a vast area under sundry Arab dynasties, from the
Ebro River in Spain across to the Nile and thence eastward
to Central Asia. Luxury, complex bureaucracy, advanced, "lei-

sure-class" art and science characterized some of these dynasties. In the ninth century, when Charlemagne and his princes in Europe were scarcely able to write their own names. Harun al-Rashid was reading the philosophic works of Plato. But while it is generally true that the Arabs enriched the sciences, chiefly mathematics and chemistry, with new ideas and methods, they collected most of their knowledge according to the Greek pattern—that is, by quoting and theorizing from the (translated) Greek masters.

With a broad-minded spirit of freedom, the Arabs did not exclude people of foreign origin from their cultural life, nor even people of a different faith. The only forbidden thing ·was inciting to rebellion, and all knew the truth of the Talmudic injunction: "If the fox is king, the lion must bow."

Under the intellectual authority of the Greek classics the Arabs assiduously broadened the boundaries of their outlook. In the tenth century comprehensive medical works began to appear in which specifically Arab material was included in a Hippocratic and Galenic framework. But, while the Arabs added countless new methods to medicine and surgery their anatomical knowledge remained static. And since a knowledge of the exact nature of the various organs was lacking, they were obliged to follow in the well-trodden footsteps of Galen when investigating organic function. Yet function cannot be discovered without a precise knowledge of the nature of the organ!

* * *

Dissection was considered an undesirable practice and was, in fact, forbidden, which explains why there was nothing fundamentally new on the anatomical structure of organs in Ibn Sina's (Avicenna) famous medical encyclopedia. In view of this accepted ban on dissection it was quite natural that, for the students at the Nuuri hospital in Damascus around 1230, Ibn Sina's books should appear as the unequalled source of knowledge.

One of these students was Abu al Abbas Ahmed Ibn Abu Usaibiyaa and another, Abu al Hassan al Kurashii Ibn al Nafiis. In addition to the medical sciences they studied botany, astronomy,

law, literature, mathematics, philosophy, and the Koran. When
at the end of their student years they went to Cairo, seat of the
caliphate, the two friends once again worked in the same hospital. In addition to their compulsory studies each had his own
favorite hobby. Usaibiyaa studied history and corresponded
with the famous Abd al-Latiif of Baghdad. Nafiis, on the other
hand, was drawn by the never-ending questioning and doubting discourses of philosophy. But every morning they did their
hospital rounds together; and together they sought a solution
to the problem of trachoma.

Later, the two friends went their separate ways. Al Nafiis remained in Cairo and, no one knows why, Usaibiyaa moved to
Salkhad, a small city on the edge of the Syrian desert, leaving
the rich possibilities offered by the capital for a place of neglect
and oblivion.

As the years passed the fame and prestige of Al Nafiis grew.
He was named "Egypt's Prince of Doctors" and when the Caliph
Kalawuun had a hospital built in Cairo to commemorate his
recovery from an illness, Al Nafiis became its director. The
hospital, Al Maristan al Masuuri, was equipped with the latest
technical devices, including central heating. It did not consist
solely of hospital buildings, but made up an entire university
according to the Arab pattern, with its mosque, school and library, where Al Nafiis could teach law and philosophy in addition to medical subjects. His universal interests and knowledge put him in the ranks of Aristotle and Ibn Sina. Of the
many books he wrote, most of which have since perished,
ten dealt with medical subjects.

Meanwhile Usaibiyaa was not idle on the edge of his desert.
He wrote a history of medicine, including a detailed biography
of four hundred Greek and Arab physicians up to his own
days. The name Al Nafiis is not mentioned in it. Usaibiyaa had
lived in personal contact with him and could have given some
account of his habits, but he remained silent. Why we do not
know.

* * *

In the free time left to Al Nafiis after his law lectures and
hospital duties he studied anatomy. Although an experienced

and well-known physician, he preferred abstract questions to dealing with patients—questions which appeared to have no possible connection with the complaints of sick people. He gave vague answers 'to those seeking cures. Perhaps he did not even listen, or perhaps he was ashamed to hide his lack of conviction by pretending to a positiveness he did not feel.

On one occasion, when asked for his definite opinion on a particular form of treatment, he gestured sadly and remarked that he too had something wrong with him and had no idea how to treat the complaint. No one understood the motives behind his vagueness but it certainly did nothing to enhance his reputation. A physician who is sick and unable to cure himself! How then could he be expected to save others?

Another thing which might have increased his unpopularity was the fact that he was a bachelor. In the Caliph's city, the more wives he possessed the greater his prestige would have been, yet he had none at all. A man about whose love life nothing was known, what sort of a man could that be? The little book on "The Art of Love" by Moses Ben-Maimon (Maimonides) had recently appeared, and the booksellers made good business by having it copied. Yet Maimonides too was a scholar, a famous rabbi, a student from the famous University of Cordova.

Al Nafiis, completely indifferent to the impression he made, returned to his studies the moment he left the hospital. The Caliph held him in high esteem, so what did the opinions of the ignorant mob matter to him?

It was probably as a result of his examination of the carcasses of monkeys that it occurred to him that the partition dividing the ventricles of the heart (interventricular septum) was too thick and tough to permit the flow across it, as claimed by Galen. The tissue of the ventricular partition when cut was no different from the walls of the ventricles themselves; thus, if blood did not penetrate the walls, why should it penetrate the septum? Yet if it did not go from the right ventricle into the left, then the entire, old conception of blood flow was wrong, in which case it had to be concluded that other statements made by Galen were also false.

Al Nafiis could not devote too much time to studying the heart and could not openly experiment with live animals nor dissect

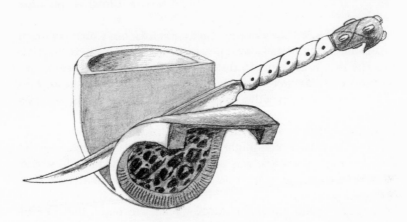

17. Cross section of septum between ventricles. (By A. Barabas)

human bodies, for these practices were in conflict with the teachings of the Prophet Mohammed. Consequently, he had to exercise the greatest care in wording his differences of opinion with the old masters, and had to disguise the "crime" of his dissecting with an appearance of compliance so as not to offend the existing laws.

"Our aim," he wrote in the introduction to his book on anatomy, "is to pursue what we already know from the anatomical expositions of the Canons of Sheik Ali Al Hussein Ibn Abdullah Ibn Sina (Avicenna), and by summarizing the contents of the first and third books, to classify what he wrote on the subject of anatomy. We were held back from dissection by our respect for the law and our inborn compassion. We therefore thought it proper in describing internal organs, to uphold the words of those before us, who had practiced dissection, particularly the revered Galen, since his books are the best on this subject among those at our disposal."

The Moslem student reading this would find nothing objectionable in the words of the director of Al Masuuri, nothing to incite against respected canons. And thus Al Nafiis presented himself in gentle humility, hiding his sharp vision behind a mask of obedience. This was important, for in the next sentence he turned to attack softly but inexorably.

"We base our assertion that the descriptions of Galen were

made after faulty observation chiefly upon Galen's own writings,
except for a few details which we attribute to errors in copying
and the results thereof. In describing the function of organs we
started out from first-hand observation and sincere studies, taking no account of whether they agreed with preceding theories
. . ."

But Al Nafiis had here to tread carefully. This was still only
the introduction, which might possibly be read by officials of the
Caliph before the book was allowed to be circulated. It would
be best to leave the refutation of errors to parts filled with dull
technical data.

"Together with Allah the All-Knowing, we teach that one of
the functions of the heart is the production of 'spiritus' from
very fine blood which easily combines with air. . . . The site
where spiritus is produced is the left ventricle. That is why it
is important that in the heart of man and other like living beings
who have lungs there should exist a second chamber where
the refining of the blood takes place, where it can be made
suitable to combine with air. This is the right ventricle. Once
the blood has been refined in this chamber, it must necessarily
get into the left ventricle where spiritus is produced. But there
is no passage between the two, for this part of the heart is
closed and there are no visible pores as was formerly held
by some . . . to allow the passage of blood, as Galen thought."

Misunderstanding Galen, Ibn Sina taught that in the middle
of the septum between the ventricles, one single broad funnel-
shaped opening led from the right ventricle into the left! Therefore Al Nafiis was obliged to bring out his view less cryptically.

"The pores of the heart are closed at that point, its substance
is tough, leaving no doubt that after refinement the blood gets
into the lungs by way of the vena arteriosa (pulmonary artery)
there to spread and combine with air, and the purified part, still
further refined, flows into the arteria venosa (pulmonary veins)
to reach the left ventricle.

"The function of the arteria venosa (pulmonary veins) is to conduct the air already mixed with purified blood into the left
ventricle. Its second role is to remove any blood left over in the
left ventricle after the mixture and therefore unsuitable for the
production of spiritus, and also to remove anything left over

from the air which might be superfluous and over-heated. Both have to leave the chamber, i.e. the left ventricle, to make room for the air which follows, or air mixed with purified blood. Thus this blood vessel returns these substances to the lungs, to be ejected with the air exhaled."

These overpacked sentences, which because of their condensation are at times somewhat obscure, proclaim the fact that Al Nafiis did not believe Galen at all. For in Al Nafiis' view blood had to flow into the lungs from the heart, and could only return to it after seeping through the lungs. There could be no question of the blood simply trickling from one ventricle into the other.

When Al Nafiis wrote these lines he was not surrounded by piles of books, for he wrote partly from personal observation, and he could also draw at will a complete mass of appropriate data filed away in his mind. And since there was nothing to interrupt the racing of his thoughts, he returned again to the most vital question of circulation: could the blood flow across the partition between the ventricles from right to left, or not?

A denial of Galen's circulation theory, believed until then beyond any shadow of doubt, could have meant Galen's complete downfall. Fully aware of this, Al Nafiis sought to leave no doubt in the minds of his readers as to the truth of his refutation and offered the proofs presented by dissection.

"Between the two ventricles . . . there is absolutely no opening, for if there were, blood could enter into the place of spiritus, spoiling its composition. Dissection further refutes their assertions, for the partition between the two chambers is thicker than elsewhere. . ."

He had now given himself away, and, careless of the consequences, pursued the truth as he saw it to the end. He shed the homage which in his introduction he had felt obliged to render the great Galen and Ibn Sina, and now proceeded to attack with almost crude directness, allowing no contradiction: "and further, Ibn Sina's statement that the blood from the right ventricle serves to nourish the heart is not true at all, for the heart's nourishment comes from the blood streaming in the vessels throughout the body."

The chief thrust was aimed at Ibn Sina, but it hit Galen as

well: It was Galen who had claimed that blood from the
veinous side nourished the various organs, including the heart,
while Al Nafiis attributed the source of nourishment apparently
to the aorta (coronary arteries).

Nonetheless, in the eyes of the world Galen's theory of blood
flow remained the standard one. In vain did Al Nafiis bequeath
all his writing to the Al Mansuuri Hospital in his will. Ibn
Sina had quoted Galen in his Canon of Medicine and that was
that. He occupied the same position in medical circles in the
Arabic world as Galen had among the Greeks and Romans.
New physicians in succeeding generations returned repeatedly
to his books; and in time the monotonous repetition of the
works of the ancient scholars brought Galen's and Ibn Sina's
voices to the attention of the students' ears more than any
others. A kind of respect based on laziness made the familiar
synonymous with true, a manifestation of the "law of gravity" in brain function which draws back any sort of outward
deviation to an accustomed train of thought. In order to make
the mind accept anything new, first some kind of disturbance
must take place, some tormenting uncertainty, some almost
threatening lack of order which is so painful as to make the
mind ready for any uncomfortable effort to escape chaos, sweeping out useless matter in the process. But, so long as assurance
is maintained, and painful uncertainty does not threaten the outlook, so long as the maddening whirl does not tear into the
soul, the mind is only able to respond to familiar sounds,
leaving others to rumble away unheard.

Al Nafiis was destined for oblivion, but perhaps not only because what he had to say was too new. A new opinion often
comes to the attention of the general public owing to the striking personality of its exponent. Al Nafiis was quiet and reserved and appeared not to care for publicity. He did not get
himself talked about. In contrast, the life history of Ibn Sina
is full of debaucheries in taverns, amorous adventures. He was
abused and gossiped about, but not ignored.

The Arabs repeated and quoted the theories of Ibn Sina and
Galen for centuries, copying their books by the thousand, together with those of the Greek scientists. While Europe, rent
in pieces, was long unable to cultivate scientific traditions, the

Arabs saved these traditions for a more auspicious era. We have them to thank for Plato and Aristotle, for the errors and surmises of Erasistratus and the boastful assertions of Galen.

* * *

The narrow slit through which the Greek spirit finally managed to enter the fanaticism in Europe was opened by the Emperor Frederick II of the Holy Roman Empire (1194-1253 A.D.).

Frederick was born in Sicily, half of which at that time was Arab, the other half under the sovereignity of the Empire. His childhood surroundings enabled him eventually to learn Italian, German, Arabic and Latin. Orphaned at four years of age, he was removed from the stupefying effects of a society of courtiers and princely pomp. Every week he took his meals with another family of ordinary citizens, and in the afternoons he played with the street urchins of Palermo.

Fredrick became acquainted with both Christian and Arab dogma and culture simultaneously. He became used to viewing Mohammendans with Christian eyes and papal pronouncements with those of an Arab. He became familiar with the virtues and shortcomings of both; and he did not commit himself to either side.

He liked the Arab philosophers and had mathematical discussions with them. He kept an Arab body guard, an Arab fleet —and a harem. Yet he drove the Arabs out of Sicily.

At the same time that Frederick considered it important to win over the princes of the Church with gifts and to have himself crowned Emperor, swearing on the cross, he disregarded papal curses. A man of great energy, he struggled for decades against the popes, secretly and openly; but he also, as it were, had time left for the erection of buildings, for writing love poems and founding universities.

He founded a medical school in Salerno in Italy where Moors and Christians had an equal voice, where women could teach just as men, provided they knew their subject. And in order that the surgeons marching with the armies should not be as abysmally ignorant as he had found them to be, he made it a law that only those could be granted a diploma in medicine who had taken part in the complete dissection of at least two bodies.

1500 years after Herophilus and Erasistratus, once again the human body itself had to be studied if information about human anatomy were to be acceptable.

In its long struggle against Frederick, the Papacy was scarcely successful. It looked to many as if the pope was not all-powerful, or invariably right. True, after the death of Frederick, his Empire fell to pieces; but his laws and the memory of his boldness and independence remained.

The practice instituted under Frederick, of dissecting the human body into small parts so that each detail could be studied, spread as the accepted practice in the study of anatomy. Some, of course, were still reluctant and fearful, and their doubts were further increased by certain papal edicts. In one decree, Pope Boniface VIII forbade the dismemberment of those who died in a foreign country, as being "a hateful and inhuman step backward." This was because the remains of bodies of those fallen in the crusades which were to be sent home had the flesh cut from the bones, after which the skeleton was boiled and packed in a case and sent home for ceremonial burial. The papal interdiction had this in mind and though it did not apply specifically to scientific studies, the overly eager critics made use of the decree whenever it suited them.

In spite of these difficulties the dissection of bodies in Italy in the thirteenth century became yet more accepted and established. But it was hard to procure human bodies. In Bologna, Mondino assumed the right to produce a book on the basis of a few dissections—of course, with a copy of Galen's catechism at his elbow.

While these timid beginnings started to break the ground for further knowledge of the human body, new voices began to be heard proclaiming man's spiritual strivings to break through the existing walls of dogma and suspicion. A royal decree in Hungary forbade exorcism and witch burning (King Kalman the Book Lover, 1119). Somewhat later, in England, Roger Bacon (around 1280), from a monastery, began to talk about devices to make life easier, carriages without horses, flying machines, and this at a time when merely to think about life on earth seemed like unnecessary temptation, for it drew the attention away from the only important thing: life after death. Yet the power of the Papacy was still strong enough to send Bacon to a dungeon because of his unconventional thoughts. The Inquisition organized by the Dominicans was but one, if the best, example of the smothering of individual thought.

Nevertheless, changes and wider horizons were soon to be seen.

* * *

In 1343-44, Europe was ravaged by an unusually severe epidemic which began in China and reached to the shores of the Atlantic. It was the Black Death, a bubonic plague of unprecedented dimensions: flourishing cities lost as much as nine-tenths of their population. One third of Europe's people died.

"What shall I say?" wrote Petrarch despairingly to a friend. "Where shall I begin? Where shall I turn? Suffering everywhere. Terror everywhere. Oh! my friend, would that I had never been born, or had already died! The sick man lies miserably alone in his home, not one of his relations dares to approach him. The priest himself is filled with dread as he hands him the sacraments. Children cry heart-breakingly to their parents, fathers and mothers to their sons and daughters, husbands and wives to each other. But all in vain!"

Boccaccio wrote in a similar vein: "Those left alive are crazy with fear and in their terror have no thought but for themselves . . . in this terrifying collapse the laws of God and man have disappeared, everyone acts for himself."

But nothing was any use, no magic potion, or amulet or prayers. Honest men died by the thousand while thousands of the wicked remained. Witnessing the injustice of Providence, men began to blaspheme against God and even if they were of a milder disposition, their faith began to be mixed with the sour taste of doubt. It was, in fact, the friars inside monasteries who died in particularly large numbers, the very men who had led the populace, or, as some held, led them astray. Crowded together, run down by fasts and flagellation, regarding any form of ablutions as sinful, they selflessly nursed the sick and comforted the dying. It was therefore natural that the epidemic should take its heaviest toll among them.

Monasteries, churches, schools by the thousand stood empty: the priests and teachers were in the graveyard. The pope was obliged to disband flourishing monastic orders for lack of monks.

In many places people were left without leadership of any kind. It became necessary for them to govern their own lives in the light of what they had experienced, without control or restrictions of any sort. They discovered from their own experience that no one bothered about them, no one rewarded them for good deeds and, on the other hand, no one held them to account for any crimes committed. And if they made a fortune, either by hard work or the judicious use of a little poison, this was by no means as unrewarding as they had been led to believe.

One hundred years after the Black Death the awakening consciousness of Italy received another kind of stimulus. The Byzantine Empire fell and was occupied by the Ottoman Turks (1453 A.D.).

Some Greek scholars and artists hopefully stayed where they were and awaited the entry of the thousands of triumphant janissaries, thinking they would offer their services to the Sultan. They were not permitted such thoughts for very long: those who put their trust in the Turks were killed. The foresighted and the suspicious, on the other hand, fled to Italian cities, and, together with their doubting minds, they brought with them an idolatry of classic Greek art and the teachings of the ancient philosophers which in Italy had either been forgotten or corrupted.

Thus the arrival of these scholars provided an impetus to study all over again everything from the laws of geometry to the heavenly bodies, from the classifications of the animal and plant kingdoms to the meaning of history and the conception of God.

Among the various interpretations of natural phenomena there was seen, more and more, only one way of finding the truth: by means of direct contact, measurements, observation and trial. And in subjects not pertaining to visible nature? These of course were hard to approach by way of experiment, but slowly and imperceptibly they also came under the influence of the changed sense of values.

The new mode of thought, the motto of which was "personal experience and individual observation," could boast of remarkable successes within an amazingly short time in art, astronomy, geographical discovery, methods of warfare, humor and self-appraisal—in fact, in every human field of endeavor. Indeed, in Italy, within a few decades, the world of the human spirit made more progress than in the thousands of years of the historic era up to that time.

We have already enumerated some of the many causes of unique rebirth (Renaissance): the flourishing of trade and the stimulating effect of new voyages and the wealth they brought; the gradual civilizing of European life; and the breakdown of the power of the Papacy; the Black Death and the newest impulses of the Greek scholars. In addition to these, however, two more factors ought to be considered.

The first is the many-sidedness of European culture. Seldom before in history had it occurred that independent and often hostile political entities, of different tongues and temperaments, should develop under the same religious culture, that of Christianity, as powers of comparatively equal strength. This similar religious-cultural upbringing made the thoughts of people, however widely divergent, comprehensible to each other.

The other factor is that the European nations reached a higher order of development at this time, just when the other causes listed above made them most receptive to the acceptance and use of this superior stage of development.

In the course of history, a curious law of averages emerges: from the time of leaving their barbaric, nomadic state, nations have required approximately 400-500 years, that is, fourteen to eighteen generations, to evolve and reach a higher degree of culture.

The Greeks occupied the Greek peninsula by 900 B.C., and Greece's Golden Age falls into the fifth to fourth centuries B.C., in other words, five hundred years later. The Romans founded their city about 700 B.C.; real Roman life developed in its entire fullness after the Punic wars, five hundred years later. Mohammed started the Arab tribes moving in 650 A.D., and the most brilliant pages in Arab cultural history were written in the 11th century A.D., four hundred years later.

It is impossible not to be struck by a similarity—however dis-
pleasing at first sight—to the mental development of rats.

Some years ago, in a laboratory of animal psychology in
the United States, albino rats were placed in a labyrinth in the
centre of which a tempting morsel of bacon was placed. Following the scent the rat, after getting side-tracked into blind alleys
and wrong turnings finally found his way to the desired morsel.
This was repeated several times until the rat learned the short-
est way. Following generations of rats, just like their parents,
were also placed in the maze of the labyrinth and it transpired
that succeeding generations learned to discover the quickest
route increasingly quickly, the maximum being reached by the
tenth generation. Later ones did not learn to do it any quicker,
but the tenth generation proved to be much quicker in its
ability to learn than its ancestors.

It would seem that in addition to the accumulation of material
goods, which makes possible in the first place the appreciation
of intellectual values and creativeness, the human mind requires
the mental gymnastics of many previous generations in order
to achieve the possibilities latent within its capabilities. If this
is so, then it is interesting to note that the European nations
also reached the five hundredth year after abandoning their
nomadic ways (8th century A.D.) at the beginning of the Renaissance (14th century A.D.), and they started out upon the road
of modern thought at this very period.

* * *

Among other European countries, Italy also had suffered dismemberment under princes, kings and the arbitrary rule of the
Papacy. There were, however, two cities which were not prepared to bow before any sort of tyrant. These were Venice
and Florence. And in these two cities the chief virtue was not
heroism, but money.

For Venice, built as it was half on the open sea in an inacces-
sible spot and barred from the mainland by swamps, shipping
was of prime importance. Thus it was the Venetians who first
ventured into every corner of the Mediterranean, trading, bar-
gaining with Christians, Arabs and Turks. Marco Polo, who went
as far as China in his search for fortune, was a Venetian. Eastern spices, gems, textiles, rugs could only reach Italy and the

rest of Europe through Venice—after payment of handsome customs duties.

In contrast to the inaccessibility of Venice, Florence was on everybody's way everywhere. If Gothic armies attacked Rome, they had to march through Florence. If they retreated, the fleeing and pursuing troops passed through once again. The brutality and arrogance of the foreign soldiers filled the inhabitants with deep hatred against any form of despotism. Finally, after the death of Frederick II, at the price of a few decades of war and revolutions during which the emperor wanted to raze this obstinate city to the ground, Florence succeeded in achieving independence.

A struggle for control of the city soon began, ending in 1444 with the triumph of Cosimo de Medici. His family was one of the richest in Europe, and Cosimo knew how to use the power inherent in his vast wealth. He was calculating, but quick and forceful in his business dealings. He generally appeared cautious; if forced, he could also be ruthless. In delicate situations he listened to the majority, but if there was some distasteful task to be carried out, he got others to do it, thus keeping his own popularity.

In a city which for decades had witnessed street riots, minor revolutions, alliances with foreign states and the breaking of those alliances, practically no one was free from financial troubles at one time or another. Cosimo loaned money freely and did not attempt to recover the sums; and after a time the entire city was his debtor and under obligation to him.

Since various harbors had come under Florentine rule, it was no longer necessary to sell goods through Venice. Galleys left from Pisa and Livorno laden with silken shawls and clothes, bound for Marseilles, London or Bruges. But Cosimo knew that the textile market was in the hands of whoever controlled clothes-dyes, and for this alum was required. By clever maneuvering he obtained the Near East's entire production of alum for himself, several hundred tons of it per year, and thus was in complete control of the market.

Cosimo was a practical man without the time to assimilate humanist culture to any high degree. But in the city of Dante, Boccaccio, Giotto, Ghiberti and Donatello he naturally acquired

an appreciation of greatness of the spirit. He founded a library
and organized a society of scholars, the Platonic Academy, the
duty of which it was to teach Greek civilization to the younger
generation. After the fall of Byzantium he invited the fleeing
philosopher Argyropoulos to Florence and the greatest humanist of his era, Marsilio Ficino, lived in his house. The sculptor
Donatello was his good friend, as was Leone Battista Alberti,
man of universal talents.

A whole generation grew up in an atmosphere of freedom, affluence, well-being and the appreciation of intellectual values.
Never before had so many artists and scholars found room for
the expression of their talents as in those days in Florence.

Art had not yet been subdivided—it represented an undivided
whole. The goldsmith's craft, painting, sculpture, were merely
different branches of the same trade. In addition, the artist had
to be familiar with the blending of colors, the priming of
walls to be painted, the planning of buildings. A typical representative of the artists of that period, Leone Battista Alberti, is
proof of the almost unlimited possibilities inherent in the human mind. We might even think that everything said about
Alberti at the time could only be the fruit of some romantic
fancies if it were not borne out by numerous contemporary
witnesses and works of his in existence to this day. In athletics
and horsemanship he was unequalled. Musicians admired his
compositions. He was in the first rank among physicists and
mathematicians; and the magic lantern, a step-measuring device, and the camera obscura were his inventions. Buildings
designed by him are still to be seen in Florence. His theoretical treatise on architecture remained an important book of
reference for a long period. He wrote numerous short stories,
poems and articles, both in Italian and Latin, which were quoted
for a long time afterwards. In addition to all this, he painted and
designed beautifully, taking care to balance his own love of beauty with the sobriety of Florentine taste.

In his book entitled "The Theory of Painting" he writes: "It is
necessary to observe exactly the proportions of various parts of
the limbs. For this purpose it is very desirable first to draw the
living model's skeleton, then add the muscles, and then round
off the whole with flesh. . . . Some, however, might argue that

only that which is visible concerns the artist. But just as we first draw the body nude, and only add clothing later, so when drawing from the nude, we should first begin with the position of the bones and muscles and only later cover these with flesh. In this way we will not have the difficulty of having to suggest the position of each muscle under the flesh. . . . Therefore enthusiastic painters should spare no efforts to pursue any knowledge they may have acquired."

Alberti's instructions regarding artistic anatomy were not given in vain. In the years around 1460 the brothers Pollaiuolo regularly dissected human bodies in Florence. Artists were no longer content with horses which looked stiff as rocking horses, or faces expressionless as wax models. They wished to conjure up remembered expressions of command, worship, love or hate in the faces of their princes and madonnas. But facial expressions were governed by the muscles which gave rise to them and from which these features resulted. It was therefore necessary to know these muscles, just as it was necessary to know the structure of a wall under the plaster, if they wanted to learn the secrets of the creation of the classical works of art. The painters dissected, the architects wandered around with a rule in their pocket, Brunelleschi and Donatello spent weeks in Rome rummaging amongst old ruins, taking measurements of the proportions of buildings dug out of the ground.

Men began to take an interest in everything around them, taking into account the carefully balanced guidance of nature and experience, using not the imagination as their starting point, but reality. They turned away from the abstract meditation of the Middle Ages, from rules taken over from others. They wanted to learn about the world as they themselves saw it.

HIGHLIGHTS IN

	History	Science and Technology	Medicine
1450-1500	Florence, center of Renaissance. Turkish capture of Byzantinum (extensive use of artillery, 1453). Christian reconquest of Spain from Moors (1492). Discovery of Americas (Columbus, 1492; Amerigo Vespucci, 1499-1502). Epidemic of syphilis in Europe (around 1500).	Perspective drawing; oil painting in art employed. Movable type printing (Gutenberg, 1450; more than 10,000 books published before 1500). New musical instruments developed (violin). Description of physical laws, instruments, machines (Leonardo da Vinci).	Dissections for artistic purposes (Pollaiuolo, around 1470). Extensive study of anatomy: muscles, uterus, fetus, internal organs, ventricles of brain, heart, etc. (Leonardo da Vinci, around 1500).
1500-1550	Reformation started (Luther, 1517; Calvin, 1535). Circumnavigation of globe (Magellan, 1519-21). Wars of Francis I (France) and Charles V (Austria-Spain).	Development of mechanized industries (glass, metal; war technology (gun shells, pistol, etc.). Heliocentric system rediscovered (Copernicus, 1543).	Injection of vessels for anatomical study (Sylvius, 1510; Carpi, 1523). Opposition to Galen; new concepts in pharmacology (Paracelsus, 1528-41). Human anatomy explored extensively (Vesalius, 1543-1555). Contagious diseases described (Fracastorio, 1546).
1550-1600	Proposition for a Panama Canal by Spaniards (1551). Victory over Turks in Mediterranean, 1571 (unexploited due to controversies of Western European allies).	Gravitational laws, thermometer (Galileo, 1583-1593). Microscope invented (Jansen, Lippershey, around 1600).	Lesser circulation rediscovered (Servetus, 1553; Colombus, 1559). Valves in veins observed (Canano, 1554; Acquapendente, 1574).

HIGHLIGHTS IN

	History	Science and Technology	Medicine
1550-1600 (cont.)	Destruction of Spanish Armada (1588). England of Queen Elizabeth (1558-1603).	Book on electricity and magnetism (Gilbert, 1600).	Revival of surgery (Ligature of vessels, etc.; Pare, 1573). Concept "circulation" coined; return of blood in veins suspected (Cesalpino, 1559-1568).
1600-1650	Thirty Years War in Europe (1618-48). Independence of Switzerland and the Netherlands (1648). North American settlements (Jamestown, 1607; Plymouth, 1620). English Revolution, Civil War (1641-48).	Description and introduction of new machines ("car without horses", steam-engine, magnetic telegraph, etc.). Optical, astronomical laws, instruments (Galileo and Kepler, 1604-37). Logarithmic charts (Napier, 1614); slide rule (Gunther, 1624). Optical laws (Descartes, 1637-40).	Theory and experimental proof of blood circulation (Harvey, 1616-28). Gynecological forceps invented (Chamberlain, 1647).
1650-1700	Reign of Louis XIV of France (1661-1715). Expulsion of Turks from Austria-Hungary (1699). Expansion of Russia in Europe and Siberia (Czar Peter the Great, 1689-1725).	Royal Society in London founded (1662). Laws of electricity and gases (Boyle, 1668-75). Calculus described (Newton, 1666; Leibnitz, 1675). Gravitational, optic laws of Newton (1666-87). Wave theory of light (Huyghens, 1678).	Living creatures arise from ova (Harvey, 1651). Lymphatics discovered (Rudbeck, 1651). Capillary vessels discovered (Malpighi, 1661). Red blood cells described (Swammerdam, 1658; Loewenhoek, 1673).

CHAPTER FOUR

LEONARDO DA VINCI

■

Heated arguments arose sometimes in Verrochio's Florentine studio between his two most talented pupils. They were discussing various methods of painting the landscapes which served as background for portraits. One of them, Botticelli, considered this unimportant, a mere trimming, for if the subject of the painting was the human face, then why bother with mere decoration?

Leonardo da Vinci, the younger of the two, examined the trees surrounding Botticelli's figures with uncomfortably penetrating eyes. These, in spite of their distance, remained stiff and lifeless, as did the streams which lay motionless as glass in their beds, and in these he found the proof he sought: he who does not observe nature will be unable to paint a decent landscape, a point which did in fact remain one of Botticelli's weaknesses even in later years.

Leonardo spent long hours drawing a flower from every angle, or would return again and again to a fragment of textile stiffened by wet plaster of Paris, to learn how to recreate its folds and the shadows made by them in a lifelike manner.

This plaster of Paris method was an invention of Verrochio's to enable his students to return to any material used as a model exactly as they had left it.

Verrochio seemed enamored of plaster of Paris. Casts of leaves, arms, hands, lay around in every corner of the studio. He even had impressions made of the faces of the dead in order to record the features for a mausoleum or monument. Beauty was truth and truth meant lifelike representation. The artistic ideal of the period was to render a lifelike picture of a chosen subject, with the composition well-proportioned and harmonious and imbued with inner significance.

In the rival studio of the Pollaiulo brothers from which Botticelli had come they dissected bodies, which was bound to interest Leonardo. Nevertheless, he did not yet leave his master. There was so much to be learned from him: mathematics, music, geography and the technique of bronze casting. Verrochio was never satisfied with his existent knowledge. He constantly sought to master new fields.

Anyone working for Verrocchio had to be very versatile. There would be a commission for a monument to a deceased Medici, then an altarpiece for a church, or a cross to be erected atop the Dome of Florence, or again, one might be charged with providing the décor and planning for a princely wedding.

And an artist who could not design a building would have been considered inferior indeed. Leonardo plunged into theoretical studies, searching through the works of the ancient Vitruvius and the "modern" Alberti to learn about the intricacies of bridges, towers and war machines. He had a profound admiration for Alberti. Besides his talents, there was another bond in common which drew Leonardo: Alberti too had to struggle against the difficulties of being an illegitimate child.

Walking in the street, Leonardo would explain to his friends with great enthusiasm how the Arno river could be made navigable between Florence and Pisa, and how water mills could be built, or how the church of San Giovanni, sagging somewhat, could be lifted. People listened to him fascinated, he made the impossible sound so plausible. It was only after he had left them, that they smiled at their own gullibility.

The monks of San Donato in Scopeto commissioned him, as a registered member of the Florentine guild of painters, to paint an altarpiece. At that time he was not yet thirty. Later he painted a Madonna for the Hungarian King Matthias, after which he received a commission from the king of Portugal for a tapestry to be embroidered in Bruges, depicting Adam and Eve standing in the shade of palm trees in the middle of a field, surrounded by animals. The palm leaves and the wild flowers in the field seemed so real and yet were so graceful, so deceptively lifelike that onlookers were amazed.

He also made innovations in his Madonnas and picture of St. Jerome. These were not the lofty figures of liturgy with the platelike golden nimbus above their heads. They were a smiling young woman, or a broken-down old man, without halos, such as one might see any day in the square before the Palazzo Vecchio or the steps of the Santa Maria Novella. Leonardo aimed at more than a cleverly-captured likeness or theatrically-arranged "genre" picture. He wanted to convey an image of inner tensions and passions, the drama of the individual as well as his passing mood.

In addition to his art Leonardo constructed machines to pump refuse out of the waters of the harbor or to drain swamps. He wanted to be famous at all costs, to surpass Verrochio, Ghirlandajo, Botticelli and the others. He wanted to amaze the world with perfect creations. He could see no point in a life which had to culminate in death unless he could remain immortal.

But for all this he needed much time and monetary assistance from a state governed in a liberal manner and in which his talents would not constantly be scrutinized, where the Lords of the Signoria would not interfere with him constantly to see that he made no mistakes.

The golden days of Florence started to fade after old Cosimo's death. As an alternative to Florence, the Papal State seemed attractive, as did Milan. But instead of Leonardo, the Pope commissioned Botticelli, Ghirlandajo and Perugino to paint his chapel in Rome.

He therefore went to Milan, where Lodovico Sforza made him a tempting offer—for an equestrian statue of his father.

No sooner did he arrive in Milan and set about demonstrating
to Lodovico that everything he had written about himself in
his letter of introduction had not been idle boasting, than the
plague broke out once again. The epidemic raged for a year
and in the city alone some fifty thousand people died.

Works already started were left unfinished, for there were more
important matters to attend to than the arts. Airy streets needed
to be built to replace the pest-infected alleys and the pools of
filthy sewers needed to be drained to prevent epidemics from
ever breaking out again.

Leonardo prepared a mass of plans for a modern city complete with sewers and separate sidewalks for pedestrians so that
the dirt of chariots and horse droppings should not soil them.
But Prínce Lodovico did not put any of his plans into effect.

Leonardo had to devote himself to the equestrian statue, since
that was what he had been commissioned for. For this, of course,
he first needed an exact knowledge of the proportions of a
horse, its muscles and joints. Sketchbook in hand he observed
the Arab thoroughbreds day after day, as they started, halted,
reared.

It was also during these years that he embarked upon his studies of the human body in the dissecting room of one of the
hospitals, since "Necessity obliged the painter to learn something of bones, the supporting framework and columns of the
flesh surrounding them." "The painter who knows the nature
of nerves and muscles will know, when a limb is moved, which
nerves will have caused that movement and which muscles will
have caused its shortening."

He tried in vain to gain an exact insight into the composition
of the muscles, for as he cut through layer after layer the one
on the surface hid the nature of the next one underneath. Some
other means had to be found to determine the relation of the
various layers to one another. But how was this to be done? He
had an idea: "Before drawing the muscles draw a thread in
their place giving the position of the layers. This will enable
you to understand a little more about them when you want
to make them perceptible one above the other."

The object of these detailed studies was to enable him to recapture as perfectly as possible the momentum of movement

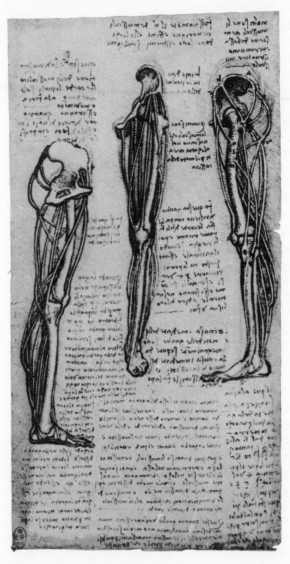

18. *Sketches of legs with wires in place of muscles.* (*L. da Vinci Quaderni d'anatomia V. Fol. 4. R*)

and to be able to convey an impression of "man and the passions in his soul." That is why he wandered among the distorted faces in lunatic asylums, why he frequented the dives of the slums, habitations of cutthroats and prostitutes, why he observed the cries and expressions of the vendors in the market place.

With a few pencil strokes he recorded the foaming rage or evil grin, for "the soul is tied to the body, unable to react or perceive without bodily organs." If he received too many impressions at once and did not have time to make a sketch, he would note the type of nose, brow and lips by means of numerals. Then at home he would re-examine them and transform them into a drawing from his artist's shorthand.

He first made his anatomical studies from the point of view of the painter. But soon he came across something which was of no importance to him as a painter, yet which filled him with stimulating thoughts.

Once he dissected a pregnant woman. When the uterus was cut open the embryo lay before him in its own peculiar drawn-up position. Did it breathe? Did its heart beat?

He dissected the embryo and observed that its liver had a different shape from that of an adult. In the next moment his thoughts were already soaring: "To observe the development of the living organism from the very beginning! But first one must study the anatomy of eggs in the process of hatching."

In addition to the development and the appearance of the human body there were thousands of other things he wished to investigate. Leafing through his drawings he jotted down what else he would study: "The cause of the cold, with diagrams. Hunger. Ecstasy. How anger affects the body. How fear affects it. Fever. Illness. Describe the soul."

Notes occurred with increasing frequency in his sketchbooks which went far beyond the limits of artistic anatomy. He opened a heart and described it, as he'd learned from the 13th century Mondino. But he was unable to imagine structure without function and so also described the rush of swirling, eddying blood in the cavities, without bothering particularly about the words flowing from his pen. The medley of references and flood of thoughts make his sentences sometimes confused, as not a moment of rest is allowed by a comma, period or capital letter. But then these notes were for his own private use.

He looked long at the heart, remembering the Galenic principles described by Mondino, and he accepted them with the loyalty of the good student. Sometimes, however, doubts arose in him. "Perhaps the veins of the lungs do not send the blood back into the heart when it contracts and expells air." But he would be so taken up with the description of the lungs and the mechanism of the respiratory muscles that he forgot what he had had in mind in the first place.

The next time he had an opportunity to dissect, he was again preoccupied with muscles and joints and the plastics of the body. But he could not fail to observe that not only muscles are important in the formation of the body's surface. The layer of fat beneath the skin, for example, is quite different in young people and in old. Perhaps its weight was different also? He cut out a piece of each kind and threw them in water: one floated on the surface, the other sank.

He measured constantly, he wanted to outline everything by means of figures, from art to the course traveled by a cannon ball. He held that "No human research can be regarded as scientific if the conclusions reached were not arrived at through mathematical proof." He regarded painting as a science, that of visible objects. "The mind of the painter should resemble a mirror and should be filled with as many pictures as come into contact with it. Therefore if you recognize that you cannot become a good painter, if you are not sufficiently versatile to be able to reproduce with your art every form and every characteristic which nature can conjure up, then during walks in the open turn your attention to every object and observe first this, then that. . . ."

He often shunned human society and spent his time among corpses. This work was repellent and inhuman, as a contemporary wrote some years later. Hands became soiled, clothes were splashed with blood and bile. Leonardo therefore used a special pair of boots, put a leather apron over his suit and wore gloves. He prepared a clean shirt, towel and comb in order to clean up after dissecting. The powdered, perfumed ladies of the court had no inkling that the Florentine master had but a few moments previously been occupied with such extraordinary pursuits! Years later Michelangelo's father admonished his son: "Keep yourself at an even temperature and never wash yourself" —which advice Michelangelo apparently took. But Leonardo was always clean, his short scarlet jacket was never stained, the sun glittered on his blond hair and beard. Had he wanted to he could have been a courtier amongst courtiers.

These dissecting studies, which Leonardo regarded as of the greatest importance from the artist's point of view but which showed no tangible results, occupied the greater part of his time with the result that the Sforza monument progressed but slowly. He really needed an army of assistants, for he was as bored by the time-consuming necessities of the execution of the work as he was meticulous in the care he devoted to the detailed preliminary study of any work he undertook. "Composition is a gentlemanly task, its execution is drudgery fit for servants."

Prince Lodovico was annoyed by all this elaboration in connection with unfinished paintings and most of all with the equestrian statue. Anyone else would have finished long ago. It appeared that Leonardo would never be able to complete any task he had undertaken.

He started looking for a new artist, intending to dismiss Leonardo from his service.

*　*　*

Leonardo was wounded by this action of the Prince. In any case he had no great opinion of the superstitious Lodovico, who saw ghosts, bombarded soothsayers with his questions and never failed to consult his astrologer before making important decisions. How Leonardo despised soothsayers and conjurers of ghosts! In this he stood fairly well alone, for most of his contemporaries were impressed by them.

"There can be no sound without movement or vibration of air. Thus ghosts can have neither voice nor power and if they were to assume some kind of form, they would then be unable to penetrate into any place provided with closed doors."

Lodovico sought in vain for an artist to replace Leonardo—he found none.

Leonardo's vanity, enhanced by the fact that he had been found irreplaceable, made him double his efforts. He applied himself to the completion of his plans of the equestrian statue, painted his "Virgin of the Rocks" and even built a watering system for the prince's estate. In addition, in the early years of the 1490's, he made himself indispensable to Lodovico by designing costumes for tournaments and princely weddings and by supplying an inexhaustible fund of ideas for theatrical machines. It became clear that Leonardo was truly valuable for increasing the prince's fame and the glory of Milan.

He was showered with commissions. He was invited to be an advisor not only in the construction of the tower of Milan Cathedral about which arguments had been going on for several years, but also of the Pavia Cathedral, then being built. He was asked to direct the regulation of the Martesana Canal. He had to paint the princess's rooms and see to the central heating in the bathhouse in the park of the palace. Yet these were but secondary jobs compared to the effort required for the Sforza monument.

His days were oppressively crowded. While at work on the modelling of the equestrian statue he also painted the "Last Supper" for the refectory of Santa Maria delle Grazie. From early morning until late in the afternoon he worked on the scaffolding, adding a stroke here and there to make wonder, amazement, despair shine from the faces of the apostles with even more elemental force. Then he returned to his clay model and continued working on his equestrian statue. In the evenings he wandered in the alleys of the slums to find among the thieves and cutthroats features suitable to represent the depraved lines of Judas. And once when the prior of the monastery complained of his slowness, he threatened to use him as his model for Judas if he did not leave him in peace.

This incredible pace was still not enough. In the evening, before the flashlight he had made for himself, he worked on his book on "The Human Body" and the theory of painting, in preparation for which he had read all the ancient scholars and the more modern treatises, carefully screening any possible errors through the fine mesh of his merciless criticism: "Reflect, Reader, to what extent our precedessors are to be believed. While they attempted to explain the nature of the soul and the nature of life, things impossible to prove, matters which can be checked and proved at any time on the basis of experience they either did not recognize for centuries, or gave the wrong explanations for them."

In his book on painting his entire store of knowledge had to find a place, nothing could be omitted. The true painter had to be a scientist. He had to know nature—the side of a tree that has moss, the color of leaves when the wind blows against them and behind them. He had to know what clouds were like and how they were formed.

Leonardo wrote of botany, meteorology, perspective, optics, the anatomy of the eye, the bones and joints. In connection with movement, his knowledge of weight and force and ... in fact what could he possibly have omitted? Before his eyes, open to the smallest, the most insignificant, things which anyone else would not even have noticed, nothing was superfluous.

But there was more: He found time for mechanical experiments testing the impact of elastic bodies and friction. He made a new kind of loom for the textile industry and made sketches for a machine to manufacture sewing needles, calculating that he could make one thousand lire a day with it. Possibly he may have wanted to become independent of the prince's exchequer. There was no need for this, however, for his paintings and sculptures won over all those who had doubted him.

By the turn of the century Leonardo had become the most famous artist in Italy and the whole of Europe. He was forty-eight years old then. His contemporaries ranked him ahead of the ancient artists, which at that time was the greatest possible achievement. And, unknown to most, he finished his book on painting and was at work on a thesis on the subject of moving objects, the impact of bodies and the balance of forces.

Lodovico himself, who year after year had delayed paying his fee, finally presented Leonardo with an estate of one thousand hectares, "for until this time he had been unable to reward him as he might have wished, and this gift was to be but the beginning, with further ones to follow."

It seemed as if he might realize all his plans within a short time, even the most improbable ones.

However, Prince Lodovico was soon beset by serious troubles. He had made an enemy of the French, and they were determined to capture Milan. In the year 1500 they succeeded.

Leonardo wrote briefly in his notes: "The prince has lost his country, his fortune, and his freedom and has not completed a single one of his undertakings."

Leonardo also lost everything. His paintings and frescoes in the Castello were damaged, the equestrian statue which he had finally completed was all but demolished. In Milan he no longer had time, money or opportunity for anything. There followed a few months of uncertain waiting in Mantua which, after Milan, seemed like a provincial principality.

He was invited to Venice. The Republic was preparing for war against the Turks and it was felt that good use could be made of a military engineer such as Leonardo. He produced a mass of ideas useful in sea-battles; how to make sea water drinkable; how to make life belts and diving belts. He made plans for a lock across the river Isonzo so the assembled enemy troops could be drowned. He drew a submarine, but destroyed the plans: "I shall not make it public, or spread its fame, because of men's wickedness, lest they commit murders at the bottom of the sea or bore holes in ships' bottoms to sink them with all their crew aboard."

He found no peace in Venice—they could talk of nothing there but the approaching Turk. Together with his mathematician friend, Luca Pacioli, he returned to Florence whence he had departed seventeen years previously.

He completed the St. Anne altarpiece with unusual speed; and when he exhibited the panel, the whole city crowded around to see it. But painting no longer satisfied him. He had other, totally different, aims which the Florentines would probably not have understood.

He signed up as engineer to Cesare Borgia.

* * *

There were so many plans Leonardo wanted to carry out and which incidentally involved serious expenditure, that any money received for an occasional painting would not have been sufficient to supply the necessary materials. For this reason he needed constant patronage and was not satisfied with commissions for isolated works, as his fellow artists had to be.

He was preoccupied with flying for he was convinced that man could rise up in the air. He pictured what it might be like to soar up to incredible heights, like a bird flying over forests and mountains. He spent whole afternoons on the Ponte Vecchio observing the doves and seagulls as they started up in flight, following their smooth progress through the air, in order to learn the rules of aerodynamics.

For such purposes of course he needed machinery, models, and chiefly an undisturbed atmosphere. But to whom could he have turned to ensure the consuming expenses connected with such enterprises?

At that point Cesare Borgia seemed the most promising possibility. Under his patronage Leonardo had the most hope of pursuing his plans, which at that stage were still a secret.

Cesare was like a rising sun on Italy's firmament, the man who was expected to put an end to the country's dismemberment and the ravages of the small tyrants. His incredible luck and superhuman self-confidence, as wrote Machiavelli, not to mention his reputation for just treatment of conquered populations, opened the gates of one city after another before him. A great future was predicted for him.

Behind his back, but in a very low voice indeed, it was whispered that two years previously he had killed his own brother. But his speech was honeyed, his demeanor full of charm, and no one doubted his word, until it was too late.

Leonardo, however, was not interested in politics and local aspects of history except as they affected his own studies. After spending several days in one given place to discuss matters relating to the fortifications, or after making any necessary war maps, he would return to nature. He would study the flight of doves and the play of waves on the sea—seeking any natural law they might reveal. People and their actions were to him only examples of the forces of attraction and repulsion which were his real interest.

No matter where he went, and in the course of one year he visited every Central Italian city of strategic importance, his first action was to try to obtain this or that book of particular interest to him.

The bishops, earls and captains milling around him were absorbed in questions of money, or war, and it might have been expected that Cesare's chief military engineer would show at least some semblance of interest in political developments. But in his notes we find remarks such as these: "Dove cote in Urbino, 1502, July 30." Or else "Make a music machine with various water falls, like the one at the brook in Rimini, 1502, Aug. 8," or "Library in Pisaro."

People or individuals were remote from him in spite of his courtesy towards them and his readiness to help them if they asked him. Fundamentally, behind his helpfulness there was sometimes pity but more often contempt. He used people if he thought that through them he could increase his knowledge in some way, but he expected nothing else from any one.

Unfortunately, events were to leave him no peace. At dawn on Christmas day, 1502, Cesare ordered one of the city commanders beheaded. Some days later he had several of his chief officers executed.

A general feeling of terror began to grasp the citizenry. Cesare was violent and utterly unpredictable. He would often appear unexpectedly, only to vanish again for uncertain periods of time. For months he would only show himself with a mask on and the rumor was started that someone else was present behind the mask. No one knew that he was hiding the ulcerations caused by the "French disease" from the eyes of the world.*

The unexpected changes began to make even Leonardo nervous and he who usually was not concerned about his employer's habits made an agitated note in his book: "Where can Valentino be?" (The name by which Cesare was known.)

The hopes he had attached to Cesare were not realized, and Leonardo returned to Florence. Not long afterwards Italy learned of the death of Pope Alexander and of Cesare's downfall.

✻ ✻ ✻

---

*Syphilis: The French called it at the same time "maladie Napolitaine." For the unpleasant things we always blame others. Anyway all Europe (except France) called the ailment French disease and thus it was referred to in Italy.

In Florence Leonardo was commissioned to paint one of the walls of the council room of Palazzo Vecchio.

He accepted, partly because he needed the money and partly because he was spurred on by the spirit of competition, for the opposite wall was entrusted to the young Michelangelo whose name began to echo disturbingly throughout Italy.

Leonardo was then fifty-two years of age, Michelangelo twenty-nine. Leonardo wanted to show the younger man that he had not yet been surpassed by him, as some claimed. He intended this competition to be a kind of trial of forces, a self-justification, although he was well aware that he would have no easy task.

While Leonardo was at work on the fresco he accepted a commission for a portrait, that of Mona Lisa, wife of Messer Giocondo. At the same time he was at work on his book on "The Movement of Water and its Measurement" and upon problems of flying. What time he had left he spent at the hospital of Santa Maria Novella and in its dissecting room.

By now he was no longer primarily interested in the formations of the muscle and the mechanism of movement. He was more concerned with the network of blood vessels spreading out under and through the muscles, and the brain function, the foundations of life and the inevitability of approaching age.

He would sit on the edge of the patients' beds, observing the wrinkled, pale, wasted faces with the blood vessels protruding from the temples. "With advancing age the blood vessels lose their straight course and become increasingly twisted and bent as well as thicker. The question arises why the vessels should become winding where they were straight before and why their walls should thicken to such an extent as to hinder or prevent the flow of blood and whether, without any actual disease, this might in itself be the cause of death in old people. . . . These old people gradually crumbling away are using up their life force in the absence of nourishment. . . . "

At the bedside of one old man he spent an unusually long time talking and found that he replied amiably and brightly. The next day he received the unexpected news that the man had died.

What could have caused this patient's death, taking him off

without warning in the midst of an apparent feeling of well-being? The blood vessels again?

He received permission to perform an autopsy on his companion of the previous day. "I therefore made an anatomical examination to determine the cause of his peaceful death, and I found that the blood in the arteries nourishing the heart and the rest of the body had decomposed and dried up. Yet in my examination of a two-year-old boy I found that everything in him was quite different than in the old man."

For the time being these hospital visits were of importance only to himself. Outsiders were much readier to notice how often Mona Lisa had to sit for her portrait. And although the sittings were frequent, he was far from completing the portrait. Similarly, his council room fresco, "The Battle of Anghiari," was slow in making progress.

Leonardo wanted to stagger the spectator with this latter painting. To draw attention away still further from Michelangelo's fresco opposite his own he decided to try a new technique. More than once he had been able to stand out among painters by using methods never practiced before. For example he was able to lend a particular grace to faces by using much thinner paint than his predecessors had done, and by putting the color on in successive layers. Features thereby lost their accustomed stiff delineation and melted into each other in harmonious curves, as if they really lived. With his "Battle of Anghiari" he wanted to create something radically new: he chose oils to work with instead of the tempera used customarily for frescoes. Oils brought out the colors more vividly, as well as lights and shadows.

Unfortunately the central portion of the painting was scarcely completed when it was discovered that the priming had been faulty. The finished section was barely dry when the oil paint began to peel from the wall. Leonardo's hopes were shattered.

Of his three large works only "The Last Supper" was still intact. The Sforza memorial was to be broken up and, as for the "Battle of Anghiari," it had not yet been completed and was already destined for destruction.

Michelangelo observed this fiasco with cruel intolerance and his behavior was also guided by the jealousy he felt towards

Leonardo because of the latter's indescribably more prepossessing appearance. With his broken nose and squat figure, Michelangelo appeared almost freakish beside Leonardo. On one occasion he did not hesitate to taunt Leonardo within the hearing of passers by, telling him he was incapable of ever finishing anything. He did not stop to consider that his own David statue had been erected in a suitable place at the suggestion of Leonardo who could just as easily have sabotaged the project had there been any malice in him.

Leonardo felt that there was some truth in this brutal attack. He blushed deeply, turned on his heels and left Michelangelo without a word. Soon after he once again moved to Milan, city of his successes and years of promise, where things were quiet, the only difference being that the French ruled instead of Lodovico.

A few months later he had to return to Florence for a short while, during which period he drew the portrait of Amerigo Vespucci. Vespucci had first sailed across the ocean with Columbus and had since repeated this feat four times, as a result of which he began to suspect that the territory which they believed to be India must be some different, new and unknown country.

The note Leonardo made that "the earth is also a star, something like the moon" may have been jotted down as a result of his conversations with Amerigo Vespucci, and also that "The sun does not move."

In Milan King Louis XII appointed Leonardo royal painter and engineer. In whatever way they could, the French tried to please him. When the lord mayor of Florence brought charges against him for leaving his work in the Palazzo Vecchio and for behaving "almost like a traitor," the French defended him warmly.

* * *

Apart from a few minor works, Leonardo did not paint anything more. His time was occupied with his engineering studies, the completion of his book on painting and his "Anatomy" which he planned to finish by 1510.

He struck up a friendship with Marcantonio della Torre, professor of anatomy in Pavia, and studied Mondino's book, still considered the most modern, but Leonardo no longer believed him.

He trusted only his own eyes which saw so much more than did the eyes of other people.

How wonderful is the eye! "Who would believe it possible that there should be room for all the images in the world in such a small space? What words would be adequate to describe such a miracle?" But he did not linger long over such poetic reflections and always returned to the material significance of things. In order to observe the parts of the eye exactly he would dip one in egg white and cook it. Thus when he cut it up it did not fall apart and could be further examined in its original state.

He was also preoccupied with the brain, the originator of thought. But how to get the exact size of the fluid-filled chambers of the brain, said to be the repository of the soul? He pierced a hole in one of the side chambers, shook the fluid out, then filled the cavity with wax. Then, by removing the brain itself he was left with the entire system of cavities.

As for the blood vessels and the heart, he wrote: "A wonderful mechanism, the invention of the greatest artist."

At last here in Milan he would have enough time and, more important, the tranquillity to acquire the secrets of life and death. "The frog remains alive for a few hours after the removal of his head, heart and internal organs. But if its spinal cord is pierced, it suddenly twitches and dies." When examining the nervous system, he tried to discover its connection to the heart. "Follow the 'nervus reversivus' (vagus) as far as the heart and see whether it is these nerves which stimulate the heart into movement, or whether the heart moves of its own accord." This, however, could only have been investigated on living animals, which he seldom used. He felt sorry for them and preferred to return to dead, insensible materials.

He observed, drew and wrote—then began again. He was even suspicious of himself. "Nothing is so deceptive as our own judgment."

Anything he wrote down had to be right. "In order to achieve a true and complete knowledge of these matters I have dismembered more than ten human bodies. I have removed all other parts, removed the flesh surrounding the blood vessels down to the smallest particle without causing any bleeding,

19. *Leonardo da Vinci. (Self portrait in the Royal Palace of Torino, Italy)*

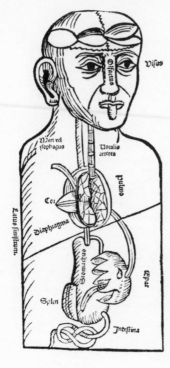

20. *Thoracic and abdominal organs drawn by unknown person in a contemporary encyclopedia published in Leipzig, 1499. (Courtesy of Ciba Z. Basel, 1943, in the article of H. Buess.)*

apart from insignificant bleeding from capillaries. Since none of the bodies kept for as long as would have been desirable I was obliged to use numerous ones until I was able to obtain a perfect knowledge of them. I should mention that I repeated everything twice, to discover any differences."

He not only examined everything twice, but also from every possible angle. "Draw the ramifications of the bronchial tubes, then those of the heart, that is those of the arteries and veins, then the third type of ramification which is the connection of these with each other. These connections, like the ramifications mentioned above, should be shown from four sides, making twelve figures. After that a diagram should be made of each from above and from below, making a final total of eighteen."

In the book he was preparing, which he probably intended to publish in conjunction with his anatomist friend, he was only willing to include data checked by himself. If his artistic dreams

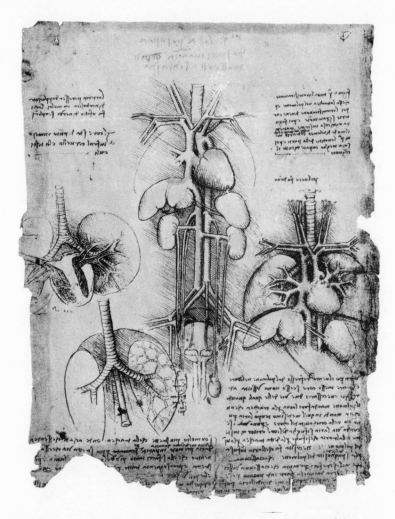

21. Organs in the thoracic and abdominal cavities depicted by Leonardo da Vinci. (Quaderni d'anatomia III. Fol. 10. V.)

had not been realized, at least this book would be perfect.

When dissecting a heart, he put down his gloves and the magnifying glass again and again to make sketches of what he saw. "Oh writer, what words have you to convey this whole formation more perfectly than this drawing? How would you be able to describe this heart with words without filling an entire volume?"

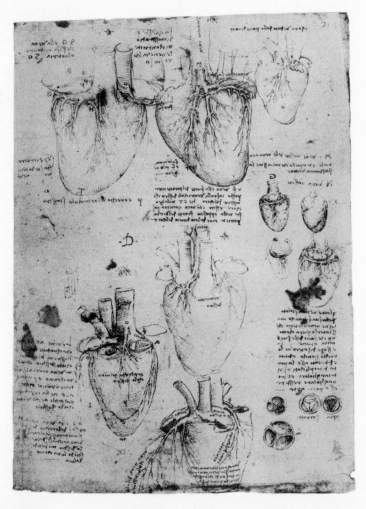

22. *Sketches of the heart by Leonardo. (Quaderni d'anatomia II. Fol. 4. R.)*

Occasionally he came across something unusual. Under one hurried sketch depicting the auricles spread out with the septum between them and with an opening in the center of the septum he wrote: "I found a hole leading from the left auricle to the right auricle, and I am noting this here to see whether it occurs in other hearts also." He had no idea that he was the first to describe this anomaly.

The difference in the thickness of the wall of the right and left ventricles also gave him food for thought. He did not believe Galen's explanation which until then had sounded so plausible, namely that the difference was to balance the left ventricle with its "pneuma-containing light blood" against the right ventricle with its "heavier blood" "There is no need for such a regulation of balance, for the heart of every domestic animal except man lies horizontally. And when man lies in bed, his heart takes up the same position. And how should the heart of the bat achieve balance between its right and left ventricle when it always sleeps suspended upside down?"

Later he turned to the examination of the chambers of the heart. He wanted to know about not only the walls of the chambers, but also their size and the shape of the place in which the turbulent coursing of the blood takes place. For this he needed to know the size of the heart in its fullest state. The simplest method was to tie all the blood vessels starting out from the heart and to blow it up by means of a glass tube. However this still did not make the chambers visible. He therefore made casts of them, as he had done casts of feet and hands in Verrochio's studio in his youth.

He still was not satisfied. The wax cast lacked movement. He therefore made a model of the heart out of glass. He surrounded the wax impression with plaster of Paris and thus obtained a plaster model of the walls of the heart. He melted the wax which was inside the plaster, poured it out and blew a red hot glass tube into the plaster cavity to obtain a glass outline of it. After cooling, he broke off the pieces of plaster and there remained the finished model of the heart's cavity in a clearly visible form. He thus made possible the direct observation of the flowing process starting out from the heart. He also stuck small membranes in the place of the valves in his model and

23. Wax model of the inside of the heart chambers and great vessels, performed according to Leonardo's technique: "Pour wax into the bull's heart that you may see the true form of this gate." (Quaderni d'anatomia II. Fol. 12. R. Wax cast by T. Doby)

24. Wax model of right auricle, right ventricle and pulmonary artery. Such a wax cast was used by Leonardo to get the final glass model in which he performed his hemodynamic experiments. (By T. Doby. Courtesy of the Me. Med. Journ.)

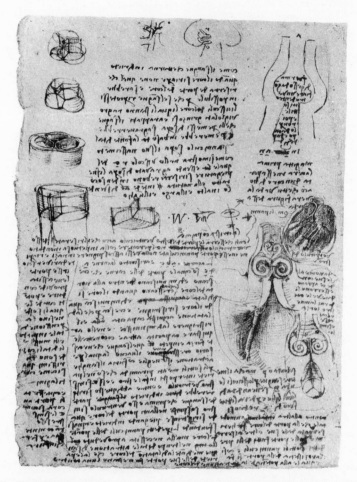

25. *Streamlines of blood in the right ventricle and pulmonary artery. In right upper corner the glass model. (Quaderni d'anatomia II. Folio 12 R. Courtesy of the Me. Med. Journ.)*

was able to study the swirls produced within the aorta and the closing of the similunar valves.

With such accurate knowledge of the valves, the question arose whether the liver was equal to supplying the blood constantly being used up on the surface of the body (as Galen had taught). For, taking into account the frequency of contractions per

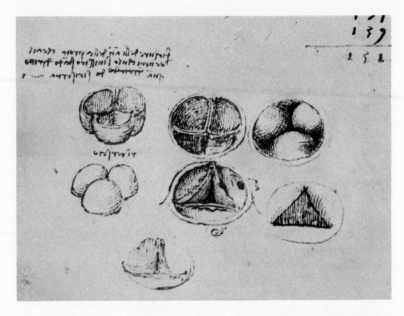

26. *Diagrams of the semilunar valves of the aorta. Second row left shows their wax cast. (Quaderni d'anatomia II. Folio 9 V)*

minute resulting from the supposed seeping of the blood from the right to the left ventricle, the amount required must have been considerable. The role of the valves therefore began to excite his attention.

He could not understand, among other things, how the ventricle could send blood into the auricle during contraction when the valves should have been closed at that moment. He repeated Galen's words mechanically, but in opposition to Galen he had to maintain that the tricuspid valves "closed completely and perfectly," and that is how he drew them.

His speculations, however, did not lead to any solution and he admitted that his doubts in connection with the valves "were very hard to explain."

If he had not put his trust in reason he would have professed the view of his contemporary Fracastorio, that the movements of the heart could only be grasped by God himself. Leonardo, however, perseveringly struggled with these secrets, for he was firmly convinced that it was possible to reach an explanation of the riddle.

Galen's teachings of the flow of blood and "pneuma" left still more puzzles for him. "It seems to me impossible that any amount of air whatsoever should be able to enter the heart through the trachea, for if we try to inflate the heart, we will be unable to blow any air out of it. . . . However I do not wish to make an irrevocable stand on this point before looking into my Anatomy which I have here at hand." When he returned to this question later his views were more decided. "The lung is not capable of sending air into the heart;" however, he continued: "it does not need to, for air is produced within the heart, which evaporates in the form of perspiration on the surface of the skin through the extreme ends of the capillaries."

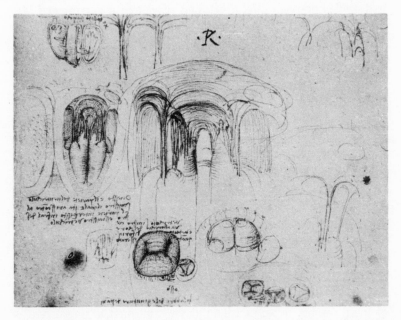

27. *Tricuspid valve from the inside when valves closed. (Quaderni d'anatomia II. Folio 8 R.)*

He rejected the theory held until then, which maintained that pneuma went directly into the pulmonary veins through the small ramifications of the trachea ending in vessels. In any case, what was pneuma? And what was air? There must exist some common factor between combustion and breathing. "Where there is not enough air for the fire, neither fire, nor any sort of animal can live. . . . Where fire cannot burn, breathing animals cannot exist either." Obviously in the process of burning some factor either disappeared or was produced. But how to find mathematical proof of this? "Prepare scales and weigh the substance, first heating it, and then after cooling."

He was not able to complete his experiment, for he was interrupted again. He was asked to make an equestrian statue as a momument to Marshal Trivulzio. Obediently, possibly forced by necessity, he began to make sketches for a statue of the man who had hated that other man, Francesco Sforza, who was the first to have such a statue made by Leonardo.

Meanwhile he received the news that both of his former patrons had died. Lodovico died a prisoner of war in a narrow cell of a French fortress. He had covered the walls of his cell with clumsy scrawls in the usual manner of prisoners.

Cesare Borgia at least remained true to himself. He no longer had his father the pope standing behind him to smooth his path; yet he showed that his legendary boldness was not mere propaganda. He leaped down from the neck-breaking height of his prison and escaped, riding long hours with both legs broken until he was able to lose his pursuers. When he recovered, he entered the army of the tiny state of Navarre as a captain. It was there in 1508 that he was killed in a brawl, rashly taking on a whole detachment singlehanded!

These events are not likely to have moved Leonardo unduly. He was much more affected by another happening, not long after.

Marcantonio della Torre, his anatomist friend, died suddenly in 1510 when barely thirty.

Leonardo sat dispirited, knowing of the destruction of his greatest works, with so many undertakings incomplete, amidst piles of many of his books, without having finished a single one of them. "I have wasted my time"—he wrote among his notes

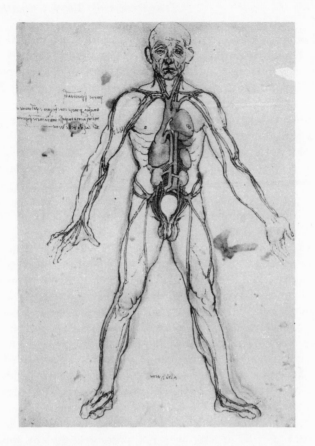

28. *"Tree of the vessels". (Quaderni d'anatomia V. Folio 1 R)*

on the heart. But he wanted to finish his anatomy at all costs and wanted to have his drawings published although he was beginning to fear he would not have time enough.

"Concerning the advantage which I should like to hand down to mankind, I shall teach you a process of systematic printing and I ask you, my successors, not to let yourselves be turned aside by motives of jealousy from making such prints."

He was filled with somber thoughts.

* * *

Leonardo had once again to prepare to move. The now grown

son of Lodovico was approaching to recapture his father's inheritance from the French. He had been a small boy when Leonardo saw him last and had painted him in an altarpiece for the family chapel of the Sforzas. But now Leonardo had no wish to meet him.

Leonardo's trunks were packed; they were put on mules and the sad procession started out for Rome.

Rome had nothing good to offer him. The presence of Michelangelo who hated him did not increase the understanding towards Leonardo there. In addition there was another still younger and more fashionable artist in Rome with whom it would have been almost impossible to compete successfully, and this was Raphael.

Nevertheless, Leonardo was obliged to start painting again. One task was a portrait of the mistress of Giuliano de Medici, younger brother of Pope Leo X. Then he had to make plans for stables to house Giuliano's 128 horses. Then the pope gave him a commission, but Leonardo was unenthusiastic.

He would have preferred to occupy himself with the reflection of mirrors and to complete the chapters still remaining for his book on anatomy. But at every turn obstacles were placed in his way. Everyone saw only contrariness in his actions and he was mistrusted. He tried in vain to make friends with Messer Giovanni, the mirror maker, who eyed his experiments jealously and hindered his work wherever he could. How could he have guessed that the old master was not prompted by any desire to spoil his trade in displaying such an interest in the mirror maker's art. Moreover, the Medici pope forbade him to dissect.

The few years he spent in Rome were filled with humiliation and malicious intrigues. He could make no progress, he was unable to finish anything. When he finally left Rome he wrote in his journal, with unusual vehemence: "The Medicis raised me up, and the Medicis caused my downfall."

When Giuliano, the last of his supporters among the Medicis, died, he quickly accepted an invitation from the new French King, Francis I, to leave the country and settle in France.

While on the long journey he was entertained by his strikingly handsome pupil Melzi, and at the bottom of one of his trunks Mona Lisa smiled mysteriously. He had never delivered this one painting to the man who had commissioned it. Was he perhaps in love with Mona Lisa?

Or with Melzi? All his life he had surrounded himself with girlish-faced young men and in his youth had been accused in court of unnatural attachments. No one made any specific mention of any relationship with women although he moved very much before the public eye, and we have at our disposal a vast amount of literature concerning the gossip of that period.

From his own words one senses a strange conflict, even dread, when he does mention physical love. "If you gave in to sensuality, you may be sure it would result in something which would bring you nothing but torment and remorse." It was as if he were fleeing from something.

Under one anatomical drawing which depicts the cross-section of a man and woman at the peak of love making, he remarks pedantically, (or perhaps in self justification,) that horrid diseases could be acquired in this way. In another place he writes that "the process of fertilization and the organs necessary thereto are so repulsively hideous that nature would lose the human species if it were not for some element of beauty in the face and feelings of lovers, and in the restraint they exercised upon their sensuality."

Whose face could it have been which induced in him emotions which made him forget his revulsion? Did it belong to a woman or a man?

He was old and fragile when he arrived in Amboise at one of the king's castles. There he was surrounded with the greatest kindness and care. Perhaps here in a foreign land at the end of his life he was finally granted that peace which he had so often yearned for and never achieved. He could draw sketches to his heart's content on how to regulate the Loire river and drain swamps; and in the fullness of gratitude he designed the stage machinery to enhance the success of the court festivals, just as he had done during his happy period in Milan. The French did not bother him or hurry him. Rather, they were proud to be near him.

The king himself, when he returned home from his amusements, would go to Leonardo to rest himself. He settled down and listened to the many things Leonardo could tell him about art, the human body and other secrets of the universe, about which no one knew so much as he. The king listened, entranced, for hours. But for Leonardo it was becoming late. It must have been at this stage that he wrote: "While I thought I would learn how to live, I have instead to learn how to die."

His right arm became paralyzed, which fortunately did not hinder him greatly in his work, since he was left-handed. There are a few drawings in existence dating from this late period. In one a slightly bent old man is sitting leaning against a stick on top of a hill, staring into the distance. He looks like one who has already seen too much to wish to see any more.

When ambassadors arrived from foreign countries the king brought them along to introduce them to Leonardo. At such times he would come to life again, and show his sketches and machines and would talk to them of things he had done in the past. From their respectful interest he saw that perhaps his work had not been in vain after all. "I shall live on," he wrote.

How much things had changed since he had left his mountain village to become apprenticed to an artist in Florence! How balanced and unshakable everything in art and science had seemed at that time! And how confused and uncertain everything had become since!

Throughout Europe, people were seized by a restless striving, a challenging doubt of previously-respected authorities. In the year of Leonardo's death, 1519, the argument over the interpretation of religious truths was started in the wake of Luther's bold challenges. The small flotilla with which Magellan planned to circumnavigate the world started out from Lisbon. Copernicus just wrote his book about the sun and the planets. The medieval dread of any mention of the human body or the functions of its organs began to fade.

The old humility began to disappear, leaving in its stead a hitherto unknown feeling: a thirsty, consuming curiosity.

THE WORKS OF LEONARDO DA VINCI

Leonardo's Places of Residence	Historical Data	Works of Art	Engineering Works	Scientific Works
1452-66 in Vinci	1452. The year of Leonardo's birth.			
1466-83 Florence	1473. Leonardo is registered with the Painters' Guild in Florence. 1478. The Pazzi family plot against the Medicis (bloody riots).	Small pictures and statues in Verrocchio's studio.† The Annunciation (Florence), Adam and Eve.† The Virgin Benois (Leningrad), The Virgin Litta (Leningrad), Adoration of the Magi (Florence), Virgin with the Carnation (München), St. Jerome (Rome), Many pictures, drawings, studies.†	Designs for the canalization of the river Arno between Pisa and Florence. Designs of military machines (tank, minelayer, etc.)	Mathematical and geometrical studies. Study of works, mainly from antiquity, on the technique of warfare and on architecture.
1483-1500 Milan	1484-85. The Plague of Milan (50,000 dead) 1492. Columbus crosses the Ocean. 1496-1504. Copernicus in Italy (Bologna, Rome, Padua). 1499. Milan is captured by the French and then retaken by Lodovico Sforza. 1500. The French occupy Milan.	Virgin of the Rocks (Paris, London). Portrait of a Lady (Cracow). Several portraits and frescoes. The Last Supper (Milan). The Equestrian Statue of Francesco Sforza (Milan) the complete-size clay as well as the small wax-model demolished.†	Designs of the re-planning and water-supply of Milan (partly executed later). Restoration and decoration of the Castle of Milan (partly†). Building of bath and pavilion in the Castle Garden. Designs of machines for the textile industry. The fortication of Genoa actuated by the imminence of war.	*Begins to study anatomy and the technique of flying. Studies in mechanics (motion, friction, the collision of elastic bodies). Friendship with Bramante, the architect, and L. Pacioli, the mathematician. Essay on painting. Plan of organizing an Academy of Sciences and Arts. Essay on human proportions.*

Legends: † = destroyed, *Italics* = works on air, water and blood currents.

THE WORKS OF LEONARDO DA VINCI

Leonardo's Places of Residence	Historical Data	Works of Art	Engineering Works	Scientific Works
1500-1503	Leonardo is commissioned to travel as the engineer of Cesare Borgia.	The Portrait of Isabella d'Este (Paris)	Design of the Isonso defence line against the Turk. Designs of hydraulic machinery (submarine, life-belt, etc.)	*Essay on the flight of the birds.* Aerodyn, principle of reciprocity.
1503-1507 Florence	1499-1504, Voyages of Amerigo Vespucci.	The portrait of Amerigo Vespucci† Mona Lisa (Paris) St. Anne (Paris) The Battle of Anghiari†	Detailed design of the canalization of the Arno, commissioned by the council of Florence.	Design of an AIRPLANE. Attempt at flying. *Essay on hydrodynamics* (streams, whirling motions, etc.)
1507-1513 Milan	1511, Death of M. della Torre, the anatomist, friend of Leonardo. 1512, Mass, Sforza occupies Milan.	The Virgin Harry's (London) Bacchus (Paris) Leda (Paris)	Design of the drainage of the Piombino swamps. Design of the navigable canal of Cesena (executed later). Lago di Como — Martesana canal design (executed).	Anatomical studies, Friendship with Marcantonio della Toree, the anatomist, *Studies on the heart.* Plan of an encyclopedia of natural sciences (some parts preserved).
1513-1517 Rome	1515, The French recapture Milan. 1516, Death of Giuliano Medici, Leonardo's patron.	Several portraits†	Design of the drainage of the Pontini swamps.	Study of anatomy. *Studies on the heart.* Experiments in optics (reflection, photometer, etc.).
1517-1519 France	1519, Death of Leonardo.	A few small sketches.	Design of the canalization of the river Loire.	

Legends: † = destroyed, *Italics* = works on air, water and blood currents.

CHAPTER FIVE

VESALIUS CONTRA GALEN

■

The travel descriptions of Amerigo Vespucci, together with greed and the desire for power, or in some cases simply fear of the gallows, spurred a motley array of adventurers to join the voyages from Europe to the New World. But as the sailors sighted the shores which should have meant their deliverance they saw that the outlines of the protruding cliffs were not those which they had been led to expect. The existing maps were full of errors; and growing experience pointed to more and more mistakes. Only the astronomers could be of help.

One of these, Copernicus, who had never seen more of the sea than that around the sand banks of the Lido in Venice, developed startling theories on the basis of his calculations: namely that the earth was not the center of the universe, but a minute particle, one of many specks of matter revolving around the gigantic orb of the sun. He worked in modest retirement as parish priest in a small Polish city, although his fame was already spreading, and from time to time he was requested to submit his writings to an occasionally interested cardinal.

Many among the Roman cardinals were just as familiar with the laws of astronomy as with the Greek literary classics. But it was also their duty to check all innovations, for there were some "idea-men" who were beginning to preach religious doctrines other than the accepted ones.

Since its victory over Arianism a thousand years earlier, the Church had been consolidating its dogmas. Religious life and law had grown, becoming more complex and comprehensive and, as it were, indisputable. There was an official explanation for every question relating to the life and teachings of Christ. Such periodic dissenters as John Huss had to be destroyed at all costs, for the incontestability of the dogmas of faith was vital to the authority of the Church. But with the broadening of worldly knowledge philosophic questions and doubts increased; until finally the question of salvation began to be argued.

Luther's ten points were but the spark which started the conflagration. The venerable edifice of the Roman Church was having firebrands hurled at it from the most diverse quarters. Within a few years voices were raised in favor of Luther in numerous parts of Europe. Eventually, the turbulent process that split the Church and brought forth Protestantism gained so much momentum that literally almost everyone in Europe was affected. Every man, in some way, had to declare himself for Luther or against him. Moreover, many began to study the Bible, and not under the direction of the Roman Church.

Within a few years, the question of salvation was being debated far and wide; the papal court came under criticism together with the Papacy itself, until then inviolable. In earlier times, at one word from the pope, kings were actually forced to stumble barefooted in the dust of the highways to appear before him and as repentent sinners to implore his pardon. Yet now every cobbler's apprentice assumed the right to express his opinion of him and things concerning him, that is, matters of a spiritual nature. But what was even more dangerous was that they began to pick quarrels with their feudal lords and sovereigns. If this rebelliousness were to go any further, tremendous chaos would result.

Matters had to be dealt with radically.

The Emperor Charles V summoned Luther to Worms to make a statement. The Emperor was but twenty-one years old, and would most probably have preferred to spend his time at dances or hunts, instead of which he was compelled to display the wisdom of an old seer and the caution of a cunning diplomat.

At Worms the papal nuncio exercised all his powers of persuasion to induce Luther to withdraw his writings. After several months of temporizing and protracted debates so boring that the members of the assembled orders constantly escaped to participate in an occasional friendly tournament, the memorable and final day dawned. Luther made his declaration before the silent rows of the assembled princes, cardinals, earls and preachers. In a voice trembling with conviction he said: "Unless I am convinced by the testimony of the Scriptures or by an evident reason . . . I neither can nor will revoke anything, seeing that it is not safe or right to act against conscience. God help me. Amen."

The Emperor replied the following day. In his speech, equally ringing with conviction, he said: "I am determined to throw in my kingdoms, my friends, my body and blood, my life and soul. I shall regard him from henceforward as an obdurate heretic and trust that all of you good Christians will also do your duty."

The die was cast. . .

* * *

In 1521, the year of the great controversy at Worms, a book was printed in Bologna which was later followed by supplements. Apart from the fact that their author, Berengario Carpi, was very pleased with them, they did not create much of a stir. They quoted Mondino and Galen by the page, as was proper. The diagrams of the skeleton were reminiscent of the illustrations for the ballad of the dance of death, complete with scythe, as it lurked leering wickedly behind an innocent child or a king.

There was but one experiment in them which was new of its kind: Carpi had tried to understand the function of the kidney by injecting water into the kidney's vein in order to see where the water came out. The method was slightly reminiscent of Leonardo's perfusion experiments, with which Carpi was most

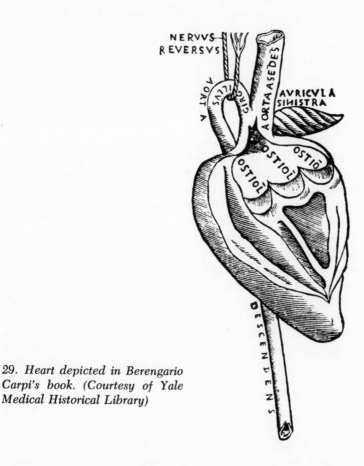

29. *Heart depicted in Berengario Carpi's book. (Courtesy of Yale Medical Historical Library)*

probably familiar. For although Leonardo's data were not published, his drawings were well-known not only to artists, but to anatomists, and being Italian, Carpi might easily have come across them. With the aid of the injected water Carpi attempted to create an artificial flow in the blood vessels and thus to follow the route taken by the blood. The results showed nothing of real value; yet the method was quite original.

A remark of Carpi's concerning the septum separating the heart's ventricles was also interesting, although he himself did not attach much importance to it. "It is strange," he wrote, "that while in cow hearts the holes through which the blood flows from the right ventricle into the left are plainly visible, in human hearts they are invisible to the naked eye."

Meanwhile, of course, Galen's explanation of blood flow had not been changed one iota. Carpi quoted him, swore by him, but when quite incapable of explaining away certain discrepancies between his findings and those of Galen, he risked a quiet suggestion that Galen may, perhaps, sometimes, have been wrong. A modest little sentence lost in the flood of praise. But it was a beginning. A few years later, in 1527, a wandering eccentric physician appeared in the city of Basel. His unkempt appearance led one to expect an insignificant personality. But anyone who heard him talk was soon overpowered by his varied knowledge, though chiefly by his conceit. His very name proclaimed his self-importance. It was nearly as long as that of a Spanish grandee, or a Turkish grand vizier: Theophrastus Bombastus Paracelsus von Hohenheim.

He lived in the home of a medical student named Herbster, who was his assistant as well. Herbster was not unreservedly pleased with his master, however learned he might be. When the latter came home drunk, not an infrequent occurrence, he would start brandishing his sword, until the poor student never knew when a blow would land on him. He would start talking arrogantly of the errors of both pope and Luther and of how he himself would soon set them straight, for obviously they did not truly know the Scriptures.

Then he would start to dictate. To Herbster's great surprise his thoughts were clear, logical and ordered.

The new term was about to begin, and Paracelsus posted his invitation to the students in the university. "Who is there who does not know that most physicians today make erroneous diagnoses, to the great detriment of the patients, by sticking too slavishly to the words of Hippocrates, Galen and Avicenna, just as though their words were uttered like oracles from Apollo's three-legged stool, and from which they must not deviate an inch. If God wills it, it is possible by such means to obtain brilliant doctor's degrees, but such people will never become real physicians. A physician needs not titles, or powers of persuasion, not linguistic ability or the reading of countless books—no matter how interesting these may be—he needs a deep insight into natural phenomena and the secrets of nature, besides which everything else becomes without importance."

His colleagues in Basel were not pleased. But his real attack was yet to come.

St. John's day followed soon after, the feast day of tricks and jokes since ancient times. After a great flow of beer and much laughter evening came. A bonfire was made in the center of the city and whatever the people wished to be rid of was thrown upon the flames: symbolic witch dolls, old love letters, whatever anyone had no further use for.

Paracelsus also appeared in the main square, followed by his students. They were carrying huge folios which he himself threw upon the crackling logs. Galen's name was written on most of them.

After that Paracelsus did not remain long in the city. In any case, belief in Galen's infallibility was being shaken.

* * *

At the beginning of the 1530's the students in Paris took to nailing mocking and impertinent little verses on the walls of the streets, or even the gate of the Sorbonne at night. They even made rude remarks about the Holy Mass. On one occasion a popular statue of the Virgin Mary was found broken into fragments. This enraged both the authorities of the Sorbonne and the parliament, and although the colleges of the University enjoyed autonomy, an investigation was begun.

The culprit was not caught, for which fact the king's sister, Marguerite de Navarre, may have been partly responsible, as she defended Protestants whenever she could. Otherwise, the perpetrator would surely have been caught and burned at the stake, with the rebellious students forced to watch "for the benefit of their bodies and souls."

The statue was remade with silver and taken to Notre Dame Cathedral in a procession, to be consecrated in the king's presence.

Although officially taking sides with the Sorbonne, that is the Church, in the matter of the statue of the Virgin Mary, the king allied himself with the Protestant German princes against the Catholic Emperor Charles. In 1532, in Nuremberg, Charles was forced to grant freedom of worship to Protestants. Thus the "heretical" teachings not only spread but sprouted new branches, giving rise to opinions which were too extreme even for Luther.

It seemed that now everyone discussed religion and expected to be heard. The threats of the Sorbonne were quite in vain. Within the walls of the University of Paris the enemies of the old faith throve and flourished.

During sleepless nights in 1532 an ascetic-looking young man named Calvin, at the College Montaigne, wrote his religious treatise, Institutio Christianismi, giving therein an entirely new interpretation to Christianity. Calvin spent his days in fervent arguments, discussions, study. Sometimes he would go to the neighboring College Sainte Barbe to win himself supporters among the Spaniards and Portuguese. There, a Spaniard from Navarre lived, a tall thin hidalgo named Francis Xavier. His chief pride was in holding the record for high jump on the athletic field. He was not greatly interested in theology, although he listened to the secret arguments of the reformers he liked to some extent.

This nonchalant, somewhat careless youth, who had no very clear idea what he should do with himself, one day received a roommate, a small fellow with a limp and large, friendly eyes. His name was Ignatius of Loyola, he was also from Navarre and, like Francis, was a Spanish noble. He had moved from the College Montaigne where Calvin lived.

Francis did not like Ignatius and wished to be rid of him, which did not bother Ignatius in the least, as he was tough and persistent. A former army officer, he was quite familiar with discipline and self-control and if he wanted something very badly, he got it, even if he had to wait several years for results. He was not chilled by the reserve displayed by Francis and finally won him over to his cause—although he later admitted that "Francis Xavier was by far the hardest dough he had ever had to knead."

In 1534 Ignatius, Francis and five others, including one Jew, swore one after the other to offer their services to the Papacy, to preach the Gospels anywhere required, including amongst the Turks, or "other tyrants who are the enemies of Christianity."

During the same period Calvin, who had just previously been banished from Paris, reappeared there in disguise. His old companions kept him in hiding and in spite of the risks, they held secret meetings. Behind closed doors and windows the cause of the new Christianity was discussed in an atmosphere tense with the fear of discovery.

To one such meeting Calvin invited a reformer called Servetus who had published a book on the holy Trinity when he was barely twenty. Certain of his statements were repugnant to Calvin. It was known to some that Servetus was "hiding" in the University as a medical student under a false name. He worked in the department of anatomy and studied the aorta and pulmonary arteries with great concentration. Such matters, of course, were outside Calvin's province, he but wanted to discuss religious matters with Servetus. He sent him a message and waited for him at the head of his little group. The hours went by; Servetus did not come.

Many years were to pass before destiny brought them together after all.

* * *

The teachings of Galen had an undisturbed reign almost as ancient and certainly much smoother than Christianity's. The Parisian medical student was given the same anatomical lectures by Professor Sylvius as had been given to students 500 to 1000 years earlier.

Professor Sylvius would sit in the center of the lecture hall, reading from a text book and would add his own explanations. He asked for high payments, and anyone who did not pay in time would be excluded from the colleges. He was a miser, every one knew that. He could have become a professor much sooner had he not begrudged the money to be paid for his doctorate, waiting as he did until his fifty-third year before finally taking the step.

At his lectures he did his best to demonstrate whatever possible, but he himself seldom touched anything. In his off-hand manner he would tell the barber to hold up whichever organ he required. The barber did not always understand what was wanted, would hesitate and make mistakes, as he was more at home with shaving and wigmaking. Sylvius for his part did not care to soil his hands with a knife or forceps and least of all with pieces of a corpse.

30. *Sylvius. (Courtesy of the Department of Anatomy, Yale University)*

The situation was much the same with Professor Gunther von Andernach. He never, under any circumstances, took a dissecting knife in his hand.

Sylvius and Andernach would read aloud from the textbooks, unaware of the attention with which one of their Flemish students observed their every movement and word, inwardly drawing a line between what he accepted and what he rejected.

This modest, silent youth was Andreas Vesalius, son of the chief apothecary of the Emperor Charles V's court in Brussels. His ancestors had been mostly physicians and apothecaries, and the family often discussed medical matters at home. During his childhood, in the middle of games, he would often think

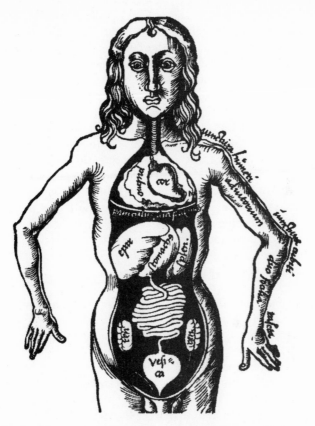

31. The "Marguerita Philosophica" contemporary science textbook from which young Vesalius was taught the arrangement of organs at school. (Courtesy of the Yale Medical Historical Library)

about matters which his playmates had never noticed. The striated texture of the cow's bladder used during swimming lessons as a life preserver was not given a second glance by others; but Andreas observed it so exactly that he never forgot it.

As a young man, he was not content with the natural history material offered at school. He would on his own catch and skin small animals, then open them to see what was inside them. The mouse, the mole were followed by larger animals, dogs and cats. With stubborn enthusiasm he cleaned and compared their

various internal organs. He became so accustomed to the sight
of these, was so familiar with the cold feel of dead bodies, that
in Paris during his student days he fearlessly roamed the ceme-
tery of St. Innocent at night in search of bones.

He worked the disproportionate absorption, with passionate
concentration, recognizing no obstacles. He cared nothing about
the prohibition of the authorities who held that the permission
to dissect bodies given to the medical faculty of the higher seats
of learning for the purpose of instructing the young could not
possibly be given to a single student for his own amusement.

Ignoring dangers he calmly searched the graveyards. Anything
he found he took home with him, cooking the bones bare, scraping off any adhering pieces of flesh. He examined minutely
every little dent or roughness in order to be able to bet with
his companions the next day which of them could tell blind-
folded which bone was which. But it was not worth betting
against Vesalius.

First his fellow students, then his teachers began to notice him.
On one occasion Sylvius called upon him to stand up and give
the demonstration, since he claimed to know so much about the
subject.

It sometimes happened that Professor Sylvius could not find the
valves of the aorta; and in such cases Vesalius would point them
out to his teacher. Professor Andernach also doubtless felt uncomfortable when he found that in his new book he had failed
to describe certain matters discovered by his student. Andernach, however, did not resent this. He was a cheerful, benevolent man who went so far as to praise Vesalius in his book as
"A young Hercules of great promise."

Vesalius was then twenty-two years old. He was proud of his
successes and it is not impossible that he may have intention-
ally and with no great modesty spread his teachers' mistakes the
better to show off his own superior knowledge.

On one occasion he himself pushed aside the barber who
helped with the dissections and himself grasped the instruments.

Members of the medical profession looked down on the barbers
—and on anything barbers dealt with. Yet treating injuries on
the battlefields, dressing wounds, opening abscesses gave barbers a certain amount of anatomical knowledge. Actually, the

official name of their guild was "barbers and surgeons." But there
was no requirement to hold the academic title of "doctor" or even
to have attended university courses to perform operations.

It was quite unorthodox, therefore, for young Vesalius, who was
to graduate from the famous Paris University, to perform the
barber's duties and hold up the organs wet and malodorous
with bile and blood.

But his life at the college was the usual: lectures, crowded
students' rooms with straw on the floor, modest luncheons of
half a herring or an egg with watery vegetables, and a pint of
inferior wine. There was never any meat at the table. During study periods the canes of the supervising seniors would
descend on the backs of the younger students. It was not a
particularly carefree sort of student life, yet Vesalius would
gladly have continued with it had circumstances permitted.

Unfortunately the political situation completely upset the tranquillity of Paris. In the Emperor's entourage the more sober-
minded tried to bring some sort of peace between the Catholics
and the Protestants, for they were merely weakening themselves
with their endless arguments and wranglings. These attempts
at peace-making, however, ended in failure.

When he could not reach an agreement with the Protestants,
the Emperor set about chasing his even greater adversary,
Francis I, into France from northern Italy.

Guns were manufactured, swords sharpened in the provinces
and in Paris. It was not good to be a foreigner in this chaotic
and hostile capital. It was known that Vesalius' father was the
Emperor's chief apothecary and that he was not French. This was
quite sufficient reason for him to leave Paris.

*   *   *

Vesalius did not remain long in his homeland after returning
there. It was perhaps a year after this return that, in the course
of a demonstration at the University of Louvain, he was accused
of having friendships with Protestants. He deemed it wiser
to go elsewhere in order not to become involved with religious
controversies which did not interest him.

He traveled to Padua in Italy, which was under the jurisdic-
tion of the Venetian Republic.

At that time, and for a long time to come, Padua was the most liberal-spirited of universities. The Council of Venice paid the professors of its University well. Among the students and professors, foreigners and Protestants were just as much in evidence as local men and Roman Catholics. To the merchants, gold was not to be despised, whether it came from Istanbul from the unbelieving Moslems, or from the Lutherans of Antwerp. Thus in Venice or Padua any foreign face or way of thought could feel itself secure from persecution.

For a few months Vesalius made rounds in the hospitals of Venice, performed venesections, applied leeches and studied the effects of the chyna root which had been brought over from America for the treatment of malaria and had received a great deal of praise.

Ignatius of Loyola and Francis Xavier and their companions also went to Venice after leaving Paris. They had given much thought to what they should name their small company. After agreeing that their only wish was to serve Christ they decided to take his name. They founded the Society of Jesus and came to be known as Jesuits. Their primary aim was the defense of the authority of the Roman Catholic Church.

Calvin was in Geneva at the same time and tried from there to shake the power of the papacy. The people of Geneva were glad to claim him as their own.

While Vesalius wandered among the hospitals in Venice the fashionable people of the city gathered in Titian's art studio.

Students came to this great artist from distant countries. Where else could they have learned such lightness of touch or how to convey the soft clinging of hair? The great Dürer himself had learned these techniques from him, and Dürer had been followed by many others. This is how Jan Stephen Calcar, a compatriot of Vesalius, came to be in Venice.

They became friends in this foreign country, and it is not impossible that it was during Calcar's sojourn that Vesalius came into contact with the distinguished members of the Venetian Council at the studio. These were later to smooth his path on many occasions.

It was probably due to such connections, and thanks to the recognition of his professors, that he was appointed professor of surgery and anatomy in Padua—provided that he first obtained his doctorate. It would have been unsuitable for him to stand up and teach students without the right to wear a doctor's cap.

On December 5th, 1537, he passed his final examination, received his diploma, and on the 6th he gave his first lecture as a professor. There were only a few days to go before his twenty-third birthday.

Vesalius' lectures were not based on thousand-year-old texts, to be learned by heart by anyone wishing to be known as a good student. The procedure was completely reversed. He first showed a muscle or a bone, and only then started to talk about it.

He drew the outlines of the bones on the surface of the skin. The sutures between the bones of the skull were painted with ink to make them more readily visible to those sitting at a distance. On the board he made sketches of the more intricate blood vessels and nerves which emerge from the tissues and then disappear into them once more.

Vesalius regularly checked the cemeteries and tried to be on good terms with the judges to persuade them not to send the condemned to the gallows mutilated by torture, or on feast days when there were no lectures. He wished to display parts of the body as little decomposed as possible, not merely because of the nauseous, sweetish stench which they exuded, but chiefly in order that whatever he showed should be as close as possible to reality, to living matter.

Calcar was present too, sketch book in hand, drawing. Vesalius kept the promise he made to his students. The subjects of his most difficult lectures, those on blood vessels and nerves, and on the skeleton, would be printed on tables measuring one-and-a-half feet to enable him to point things out clearly. Three of these drawings were by his own hand. These were somewhat clumsy and disproportionate, rather Galen-like in style. The liver resembled a maple leaf, and it was difficult to recognize the heart. Calcar's drawings were much more successful, which was only to be expected, since Vesalius remained but an amateur when it came to the sketch book. Nonetheless, his tables helped his students considerably, which was after all their object.

In addition to having these tables printed, he was already collecting material, text and illustrations for a work of greater dimensions: a work which was to analyze the construction of the entire human body, on the basis of his personal studies.

Certain sources mention the resemblance which can be detected between the drawings made at Vesalius' order and those of Leonardo. It is quite possible that those portions of Leonardo's legacy dealing with anatomy should have found their way into the hands of Vesalius. For with his friend Calcar, or in Titian's studio, it is inconceivable that there should have been no mention of Leonardo and his interest in anatomy. It might be legitimately supposed it was the sight of Leonardo's superb drawings which made him desist from having his own sketches published in his book, however much he would have liked it to be entirely his own work.

By the beginning of 1539 a few plates were completely ready, and others followed rapidly. During the preparation of the sketches he was always present, explaining, changing, erasing, if the artist did not express the object in question the way he wanted.

It was still hard to obtain human corpses, in spite of the fact that he was deterred by nothing if there was a possibility of witnessing something he had not seen before. His students stole bodies out of new graves, hid them in his bedroom to enable him to dissect them there. Revulsion and a sense of horror were completely absent in him, for he saw not the dead man but the interesting things contained in his body that might lead to an understanding of life.

He questioned the relatives of a gondolier at length to find out what had been the matter with his stomach during his lifetime, for he had found something interesting there when dissecting it. Standing before a mirror with his mouth wide open, he observed the growth of his own wisdom tooth day by day. He was at this time only twenty-five years old.

He compared the bones of the chicken served at table with the equivalent bones of humans. He made his fork into a dissecting hook, and when his eye fell upon a piece of textile he was reminded of the texture of the walls of blood vessels. Whatever he saw, the moon, a map, a statue, a monk, each of these brought some anatomical image to his mind.

He would witness any event taking place in the city, however gruesome, if it could in any way be connected with anatomical matters. Once he rushed to the place of execution when he heard that they were going to employ the more unusual form of execution by quartering. He wanted to see how much fluid there was in the pericardium. When the screaming stopped and the limbs lay unattached all over the place in a pool of blood, like a rag doll torn to pieces, he went and picked up the still beating heart, then hurried to a nearby pharmacy with it to be able to gaze at the last writhings in some quiet corner.

His university lectures were so good that the Council of Venice raised his salary. Not long before, Vesalius had himself been sitting at a student's desk at the university. Now his fame began to spread outside Venice and Padua after his father showed his "tables" to the Emperor, who examined them with great interest.

It was at this time that he received the proposal of the printer Antonio Junta. He wanted to publish all of Galen's anatomical works in one single volume with up-to-date explanations. He intended to engage the best experts in the field for this purpose and asked Vesalius to do two chapters. Vesalius temporized, for on his own table the drawings were piling up waiting for Calcar to engrave them in wood; in fact some were already finished. He had been uncovering Galen's errors with unabated zeal—was he of all people to help publicize this man?

Finally, however, he gave in. He did the chapters on blood vessels and nerves. But he profited as much as he was annoyed by this work: He got to know Galen and all his errors even more intimately.

A number of the students enjoyed hearing the ancient and venerated name being attacked, but others—members of the Council who attended out of curiosity, lawyers and monks—could not endure to hear this sacrilegious talk. In the discussions following the lectures, they defended Galen and attempted to bridge with lengthy explanations the gap between Galen's errors and the truth they witnessed. They drew the thread of the argument into different channels, analyzed in endless sentences whether theology was the most distinguished of sciences, or whether medical knowledge could be called a science at all, or an art, or even a craft.

At such times Vesalius became impatient. He could scarcely wait for the end. He was not teaching them any book, he did not prove anything by means of argument, but by facts. But they did not want to understand, they did not dare to believe their own eyes, for these things had never before been written down.

It was another case of the unholy holiness of the written word, the word written in the fancied past, by an author whose repute was assured by the still solid and venerated force of traditional authority. In such context, the antiquity of the author's name was itself almost a guarantee for objective and indisputable truth.

And yet many of Vesalius' professorial colleagues stood by him. Many were venerable old men who could have been his grandfather. They sensed in him the passionate desire for truth. They inspired and encouraged him to keep up his work and not to lose courage.

✻ ✻ ✻

Vesalius worked without respite on his book "De Humani Corporis Fabrica." He had more than 300 illustrations ready for the printer, made by Calcar and others, a few possibly by Titian himself. He discussed each drawing with the artists in detail, often causing annoyance. Each wanted to do things according to his own ideas and to emphasize certain things with an eye to artistic advantage, to the detriment of anatomical accuracy. He also had difficulties with the printers and claimed he felt worse than the body he was dissecting. Relations with the artists deteriorated to such a point that he did not even mention in his book who was responsible for the drawings. When roused he lost his self-control completely—which was not infrequent.

He packed the wood blocks for the printer and sent them to Basel, to Herbster, the former assistant to Paracelsus, who had become owner of a print shop and had adopted the Latin-sounding name Oporinus. (Latin was still the universal written language and it was common for scholars and writers to Latinize their names.)

Soon afterwards Vesalius went to supervise in person the printing of his 700-page book. He felt he had created something

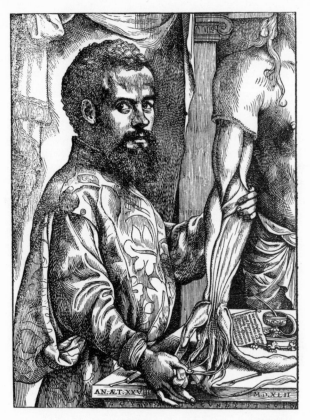

32. *Andreas Vesalius. (By J. Calcar in the book of Vesalius)*

immortal, and by no means did he conceal his pride. He suspected that a storm would break over him, but he did not
withdraw. He was incapable of curbing his ambitions or his
desire to declare new truths. "You will yet come to admit that
all Galen ever saw was the sternum of dogs and monkeys. . .
If you look at the human sternum, which appears short and wide,
you will see something very different".

He filled pages with the details in human skull sutures which he
had found to be different from those described by Galen. And
other things: the uterus did not have two branches as Galen
had taught, nor did it have seventy compartments as had been

maintained by Albertus Magnus, Mondino and Berengario Carpi—but merely one flat cavity at its center.

From the skull to the knee cap and back again his description of every organ contained something differing from the existing notions. The heart was no exception. Unfortunately, the perpetually moving heart is so completely incomprehensible if one disregards its function that in this one field, in which Vesalius was nowhere as experienced as Galen, he was obliged to take over the latter's explanations almost entirely. For he simply did not have the time to prove everything to himself, to reexamine every small detail several times over and over again.

But in one place, and this was a crucial point in the entire

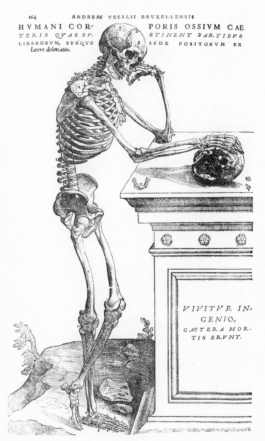

33. *"The genius lives, the rest have died". (By J. Calcar in the book of Vesalius)*

problem of the flow of blood, he expressed his surprise at the Galenian theory. Concerning the "small holes" in the septum dividing the two ventricles he wrote the following: "None of these ridges, at least so far as can be perceived, penetrate from the right to the left ventricle, in fact so closed are they that we are obliged to wonder at this handiwork of the Creator, through which blood travels by unseen roads from the right to the left ventricle."

But quite apart from professional hair-splitting, Vesalius felt obliged to reveal his attitude concerning the heart, and here he

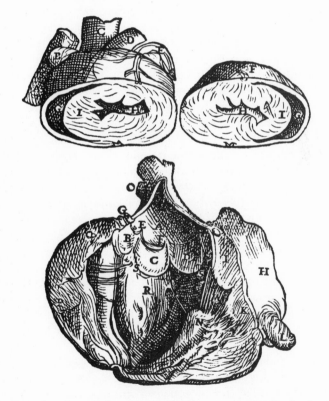

34. *Two sketches of the interventricular septum in the book of Vesalius without any "holes" in the cross section. (J. Calcar)*

was treading on dangerous ground. "The Stoics together with the Peripatetics placed the faculty of thinking and the superiority of the soul, so to speak, in the heart, assuming the heart to be the starting point of all human activity and problems . . . Galen seeks to prove with arguments which on the basis of his own judgment he raises to the level of scientific fact that the liver is the seat of those aspects of the soul concerning food, drink and sexual activity, while the mind is the seat of the thinking and governing soul. To the heart he allows only that it is the prison of the aggressive soul. But to make sure I shall not stumble into the pitfalls of rash statements, thus bringing myself up against some censor of heresies, I shall refrain entirely from discussing the seat of the various parts of the spirit. For these days, particularly here, we have come across many censors for our most holy and true religion who when they hear of people so much as whispering about the views of Plato, Aristotle and his interpreters, or Galen on the subject of the spirit, or reading about anatomical works highly necessary for purposes of instruction, they immediately accuse such persons of discussing religious matters or of having doubts about I know not what questions concerning the immortality of the soul, not stopping to think that the physician is obliged to consider all the faculties which govern us, and also the number of such faculties, and what they are singly, where they are situated in the body, and besides all this (always providing it can be grasped with the mind) they must consider what is the substance and essence of the spirit."

Since ancient times there was thought to be a connection between the anatomy of the heart and spiritual matters. Vesalius was well aware of this, and he had not forgotten the condemnation of his anatomist friends in Louvain as "the Protestants of the medical profession." He knew that the secret agents of the Inquisition were closely watching anyone who dared to express views held not to be the "proper" ones.

But he felt confident that he could allow himself certain liberties and could hide behind the Emperor's cloak by dedicating his book to him, for anyone whom the Emperor knew by name and recognized was safe. Accordingly, his foreword "To Charles V, divine man, greatest and invincible ruler" was

not without ulterior motive; but at the same time, it was para-
doxically honest, as when he wrote: "How greatly to be deplored is the very common practice in writing forewords of at-
tributing to everyone wonderful knowledge, exceptional clever-
ness, extraordinary gentleness, sharp judgment, indefatigable
generosity, special consideration for scientists and the sciences,
exceptional speed in dealing with problems and a combination
of all the virtues without discrimination and far above their
merits, like a repetitive pattern or always-identical phrase. . . . "
How did he conclude this sentence? No one before had told
kings and emperors quite so bluntly what he thought of them;
but feeling this, Vesalius then tried to climb out of the web of
his thoughts which threatened to pull him under. He succeeded, if somewhat awkwardly: " . . . Your Majesty surpasses
all mortals in all these virtues as also in dignity, good fortune
and military success (though it is but I who say this here), as
everyone can see as clearly as possible."

It is easy to imagine the cultivated and intelligent Emperor
smiling at the tangled efforts of the young Flemish scholar.

The entire medical profession received its share of the attack
that followed this introduction: surgeons lacked learning, general practitioners were but prescribers of syrup and money makers. Yet while he criticized everyone, he may have pleased some,
for each saw only the criticism of the others. Before long, however, the hints were becoming more and more unmistakable.

At first professors in general received a slight blow: "From their
high chairs, with incredible arrogance, cawing like jackdaws and
using only other people's books, they teach matters and offer
descriptions of things which they themselves cannot possibly
ever have seen. . . . " No one felt himself to be included. Yet
later Sylvius must have felt that he was being aimed at (although he was politely described as "a man beyond praise")
when he read the following lines: "Except for eight badly and
faultily dissected muscles of the abdomen no one has ever
shown me a single muscle, or bone, not to mention an exact
series of veins and arteries."

And how could Gunther von Andernach fail to recognize himself in the following? "Upon Jupiter, I maintain that in the eyes

of the careful anatomist they seem less ready to dissect a human body than to do anything else. The distinguished among these for whom I am at a loss for a name, trusting in the disinclination towards dissection in other people, compressed Galen's views into unfair and harmful extracts, and when his views are under discussion they will not deviate an inch from these, in fact they even write on the title page that their teachings are taken entirely from the teachings of Galen, merely remarking that if any one had any fault to find with him, he would at the same time be passing judgment on Galen." This remark was in fact to be found in the 1539 edition of Andernach's book.

Anticpating difficulties and feeling that the book was not to be at the end but the beginning of something, he writes at the end of his dedication with undisguised naive sincerity, with a childish impudence: "I am aware that owing to my age which is not yet twenty-eight, my endeavors will meet with little favor and Galen's erroneous teachings, for all that I mention them with great frequency, will not be in the least free from the attacks of those who did not aid me in my teaching of anatomy or who did not seriously undertake such teaching and fabricate all kinds of arguments in Galen's defense, unless my endeavor sees the light of day at an auspicious moment, dedicated in the usual fashion, under the protection of a mighty patron."

* * *

Realdo Colombo (Columbus in its Latinized form), substituting for Vesalius in Padua, did not think the latter would return to Italy from Basel, where he had gone to supervise the printing of his book. He thought it likely that negotiations would be in progress between Vesalius and the Emperor's court for an appointment. He therefore judged the moment ripe to secure for himself the position of his more famous chief, barely one year older than himself. And in order to entrench himself more firmly he began to undermine the authority of Vesalius by making sarcastic remarks about him during lectures and by magnifying and distorting his few errors and points of uncertainty.

But Vesalius returned unexpectedly from Basel. He learned with indignation that his associate, who owed so much to him and with whom he had always dealt so well, had betrayed him.

But he could not remain long in Padua. He had to go to Bologna in response to an invitation from the university there. At the request of his audience, he himself performed a dissection. The lungs and heart were the topics for discussion. He took the heart and with practiced movements cut open the ventricles. The septum between them was revealed with its small ridges which had given him so much food for thought during the writing of his book. The doubts he had then began to change to certainty and conviction. There was surely no possibility of flow between the right and the left ventricle, for the partition was shown to be impenetrable.

The impenetrability of the septum between the ventricles shook the very foundations of the conventional view of spiritus (and spiritus meant soul), of the movement of the blood, the function of the entire human body, the site and essence of the soul and . . . how many other things. For if what Vesalius said was true, where did the left ventricle get its supply of blood? And how could the spiritus vitalis, or life spirit, which supplied the entire body via the arteries, be produced?

A heated discussion was set in motion and we do not know how Vesalius fared, how he dealt with quotations hurled at him from books and eminent authorities and with the flood of talk. All we know is that huddled together (it was extremely cold in the lecture hall) lecturer and audience stayed until late at night when finally they made their ways homeward against the icy wind, and in varying states of agitation.

Vesalius hastily left Bologna the next day.

In Pisa, the Grand Duke of Tuscany was present at a lecture of Vesalius. When it was over, he invited Vesalius to the University with the promise of the fabulously large salary of 800 florins a year. But Vesalius declined: he was already under contract to the Emperor.

He thus returned to Padua and remained there a while longer, although his trunks were packed and his accumulated notes on diseased organs, therapeutic methods and prescriptions were put in large cases. He had taken leave of his friends—when the news reached him that the physicians at the Imperial Court were

spreading slanderous rumors about him: that Vesalius only understood surgery and nothing else, that he was incapable of con-
ducing a medical practice, that in fact he was not a real physician
at all and knew nothing whatever about medical science.

This blow was too much for him. He had worked too hard in
recent years, the attacks upon him within the last few months
had mounted; Columbus' treachery, the opposition he met in
Bologna, and now added to all this an unexpected conspiracy
against him coming from the very circle in which he would
have to live. He had had to leave Padua, his second home, not
of his own volition and possibly at the Emperor's command,
thus losing the opportunities for quiet research; and now he was
to be thrown to the low slanders of unknown and hostile men.

He seized his pile of notes, collected so painstakingly over so
many years, and in spite of his friends' horrified opposition,
threw them on the fire.

                                   * * *

The Emperor did not lend his ear to idle talk. He had scarcely
reached adolescence when counselors began murmuring hostile
opinions of one another in his ear. He learned to attach no importance to gossip. And though Vesalius was unpopular in court
circles, the Emperor liked his unshakable self-confidence hidden
beneath his rough manner, and so took him on.

During the summer of 1544 Vesalius supervised the embalming
of notables fallen on the field of battle and took part in the
despised work of surgeons: bandaging wounds and performing operations, things to which he would never have demeaned
himself in times of peace, for in peacetime it would have been
absolutely unsuitable for a physician of His Imperial Majesty's
entourage to perform the duties of a barber.

In time he became accustomed to his new position. He made
his peace with the Flemish and Spanish physicians with whom
he had to hold consultations on the Emperor's asthma and his
stubborn pains in the joints. It was no rewarding task. The Emperor wished to rule here also. He constantly interfered with his
physicians' instructions; and if anything went wrong he turned
to his amulets. He wore two gold rings in which small bone
fragments were embedded to guard against hemorrhoids (a most
important matter for a sovereign who spent so much of his time

astride a horse) and also a blue stone held by gold griffins, to ease the torments of gout—not to mention sundry other small stones brought at great expense from the lands of his enemies the Turks. These had the function of guarding against cramps and diarrhea.

Vesalius resigned himself to traveling from France to Brussels, to Nymwegen and Regensburg, always somewhere different, never at peace, never knowing for a moment when he would have to start out again to fulfil his sovereign's orders.

He apparently gave up his plans for a life of scholarship and research. Not long before, he had declared that he would not marry, for: "He who is dedicated to science should not marry a woman, for he could not be true to both." Yet in Brussels he married the daughter of the chief chamberlain of the treasury.

In Nymwegen, where the Emperor had left him to attend to the treatment of an ambassador, he had ample time to make new notes. Here he cautiously prepared the weapons with which to defeat his faultfinders. Ironically, he was interested only in the opinions of one man. He felt it important to get the opinion of the one expert whom he himself still thought highly of. This was Sylvius.

But Sylvius remained silent.

Vesalius felt unable to wait for Sylvius' declaration and wrote him a letter asking his opinion of the book. The reply came.

The old professor admonished him somewhat patronizingly for attacking Galen in an unfair manner—for Galen was right in everything. But in spite of this he was quite prepared to maintain his friendship with Vesalius. All Vesalius had to do was to take back everything he had brought up against Galen! This should be the easier since he could readily find excuse for his errors due to his extreme youth and the anti-Galen influence of Italian anatomists.

He assured Vesalius that he was not in the habit of abusing him before audiences. Of course the question remained as to what would happen if Vesalius persisted in his views.

Vesalius was outraged. His arguments against Sylvius became sharper and more offensive, though he had to contain his corrosive despair and bitterness.

Instead of being grateful for his courage in uncovering "all those lies" for the first time, Sylvius was criticizing him!

A letter from a physician friend asking for an explanation of the value of the fashionable "chyna root," with which he had so successfully treated the Emperor, came just at the right "editorial" moment. For the friend incidentally also asked what Vesalius thought of Sylvius.

Vesalius received the letter in Regensburg where counselors and staff officers were making plans and where the Emperor himself was sending out and receiving a constant stream of envoys in preparation for his "final blow" against the Protestants.

Vesalius was utterly uninterested in the entire Holy Roman Empire and the bloody religious wars of the day—especially when Sylvius made such impossible statements!

He sent a scorching reply about Sylvius, written at the height of fury. The explanation for the "chyna root" was but an excuse for writing. From every line came implacable criticism of Sylvius and Andernach. Everything in Andernach's book that was new had come from Vesalius. And how many errors Sylvius had made in Paris! Sylvius was plainly envious. And that he should make his youth an excuse! Or that he should put the blame on his learned Italian friends! Indeed, there was no reason whatever for him to take back anything. And in any case he had lost all desire to write books. It was for posterity to say the last word in their controversy. . . .

This letter contained far too much that was of general interest, first from the point of view of science and secondly concerning well-known personalities, for it to remain private. Soon copies were circulating everywhere, and finally in 1546 it was printed in Basel where Vesalius himself spent a few months in the company of his friend Oporinus. He would gladly have stayed, for anatomy, Galen, Sylvius, all gave them endless topics of conversation.

But anyone belonging to the Emperor's court could not follow his inclinations and was not master of his own will. The sovereign was tormented by severe attacks of gout and a courier was sent off to get the court physician.

Nuremberg, then Augsburg, Brussels, then Augsburg again, then Innsbruck — the years went by amidst the Emperor's attacks, the ambassadors' bunions and the nobility's tonsils. All the

while his rivals watched and wrote with malice, seeking his un-
doing and downfall.

As court physician and eminent lackey, how was it possible to
pursue scientific truth and new theories? How, for example,
could he hide dead bodies, how could he work alone in order to
shed light upon errors and new facts? Was he ever to have the
opportunity to solve the mystery of the septum between the
heart's ventricles—upon which depended the explanations of the
blood coursing within them?

CHAPTER SIX

MICHAEL SERVETUS & JOHN CALVIN

■

At the time back in 1537, when Vesalius had left Paris for Italy, he very likely did not know more about his colleague who called himself Villeneuve than did any of the others. They saw him at the side of Vesalius in the Anatomical Institute, and everybody was aware that he was a favorite pupil of Professor Andernach. Few people if any could have known that Villeneuve was a pseudonym hiding his Spanish name of Miguel Servede, or in it's Latin form, Servetus, the very same well-known reformer with whom Calvin so eagerly sought a meeting.

As a young man in the 1520's, Miguel Servede went to the Spanish university of Saragossa. His father, a town clerk of the small neighboring city of Villanuova, did not in the least begrudge his quick-witted son any money, for he was to be the pride and the support of his old age.

Among the professors at Saragossa was the famous Pietro Martyr d'Anghiera, diplomat and scientist in one. He dazzled his students with his talks on the curious men who inhabited the "new world," their feather-decked warriors, their limitless treasures. The material for his talks was taken from the reports sent by Amerigo Vespucci, Magellan and Nuñez de Balboa to the Council for Indian Affairs, of which d'Anghiera himself was a member. The adolescent Miguel, thirsty for knowledge, absorbed the tales about this mysterious continent, but after a while he felt he had exhausted the possibilities offered by Saragossa and wished for a more distant and larger university. In 1528 he went to Toulouse to study law and philosophy.

Following Luther's example, Melanchthon, Zwingli and others were beginning to make unorthodox declarations on various questions of religious philosophy. At the University small groups were formed in which were discussed every detail of Christ's ascension, the nature of the Holy Spirit, shapes assumed by the devil and the day of judgment.

Miguel gave himself over fully to his religious feelings, and before long he became the leader of one such "biblical circle." Finally, he was not yet twenty, he came to feel that all his reading, debating and thinking had enlightened him to such an extent that he knew what theologians up to then had been unable to grasp. Now that everything was clear before him there remained only one thing: to enlighten the pitiful ignorant souls stumbling in darkness. He therefore began to write a book called "Errors Connected With the Holy Trinity."

He was aware, of course, that it was not safe to air such views too stridently; thus in the company of "dangerous" persons he appeared as a hard working, obedient, clear-eyed, eager student, well-versed in the Scriptures, altogether a model student. The Emperor Charles V's confessor, Quintana, took a liking to him, and when the Spanish Court started toward Bologna on the way to the Emperor's coronation, Quintana took Miguel along as his secretary.

From Bologna they continued toward Augsburg with the Court. The monastic orders were assembling there (1529) to decide upon ways to prevent the Ottoman Empire, encroaching on Vienna itself, from pressing forward any further.

Quintana had no idea that his young secretary, while conducting his correspondence so zealously and receiving notabilities, wrote the following in his diary: "I saw with my own eyes as he (the pope) was being carried over the heads of the sovereigns in great pomp, making the sign of the cross with his hands. The people prostrated themselves and he who could kiss his feet was counted lucky. . . . Oh! thou most wicked beast among beasts!"

Neither the splendor of the court, nor the knightly tournaments, nor the pretty women could attract Miguel's attention. He wished to spread the truth he had discovered, primarily among those whom he considered important and worthy.

He sought out Luther's follower, Melanchthon, who was trying to avoid unnecessary frictions. Their talk went on until Miguel became so excited that patient Melanchthon shuddered at the thought of the troubles this unconciliatory youth was likely to cause.

"Good God," he said. "What tragedy will yet result from this all."

Servetus' attempts also reached the ears of another reformer, Zwingli, who snarled angrily: "There is need for great vigilance here, or else this wild and godless Spaniard's fabrications will ruin our Christian religion completely." As for Bucer, another famous reformer, he would have torn Servetus limb from limb, the only way to deal with such sinners so far beyond even the pale of the reformers.

Those rejections, however, did not discourage Miguel from finishing and publishing his book on the Holy Trinity in 1531.

It received far more abuse than praise. He traveled first to Strasbourg, then to Basel but was received everywhere without enthusiasm and even with hostility. In Basel the Protestants banned his book, in other places, the Catholics. Naturally Quintana could not afford to have a member of his staff seen conducting lengthy conversations with the overthrowers of the Catholic faith and so dismissed him.

Servetus was obliged to look for a means of livelihood, particularly since the disturbance created by his book had reached his home town of Villanuova; he also received the news that his family had disowned him and the Emperor had excluded him from the ranks of the Spanish nobility. All the functions, offices, liberties, privileges and even duelling rights which the patent of nobility assured for the Spanish hidalgo were denied him.

In the territory of the Holy German Roman Empire and Spain, therefore, there was no place for him. He had to change his name and hide behind the mantle of a lenient protecting power, where the Emperor's followers could not harm him. From that time he called himself Michel de Villeneuve and decided upon the France of François I as his hiding place.

An invitation from a Lyon publishing house offering him a proof-reading position came most opportunely. Together with Paris, Basel and Venice, Lyon was one of the chief centers of the printing industry and it was enriched by its silk and textile industries as well. Every year a great fair was held at which the representatives of all the textile wholesale merchants in Europe met. The Fuggers and Medicis maintained banks there. Lyon was considered to be almost livelier than Paris itself.

The Frellon brothers, who ran the printing works, entrusted Villeneuve with editing "Geographia" by Ptolemeus. In spite of the fact that the ancient author's geographical knowledge was already obsolete, his book still attracted readers, and its success seemed assured!

As editor, Villeneuve-Servetus pointed out the illustrious author's errors in the footnotes. His knowledge was wide, his criticism apt. The heads of the printing works were so surprised by his extensive knowledge that they allowed him a separate introduction.

Rabelais was in Lyons, too, disguised as a hospital doctor, but only in order to be able to publish his "Pantagruel" and to continue his literary studies free from the severity of the Franciscans and the chants of the Benedictines. His friend Etienne Dolet, poet and orator, was another of the readers, and so the three of them frequently met.

At the Frellon press they were in the process of setting the type for a book by a well-known physician. Servetus made friends with him, and his attention was soon directed from the wide horizon of geography to an even wider one, that of the stars. And of course, there was also much talk of the amazing construction of the human body and the fiendish power of disease. The doctor persuaded Servetus to move to Paris to study medicine. Such a talented young man would undoubtedly be a success in this field. At the time when he finally attended

the lectures of Sylvius and Gunther von Anderbach and as-
sisted Vesalius in dissections, Servetus thus had a chequered career behind him, though he hid it behind his student name of Villeneuve.

It is not likely that there should have developed any deep
feeling of friendship between the reserved and skeptical Vesalius and the imaginative and easily-fired Servetus. Vesalius lived,
breathed, ate, slept, or did not sleep, for a single, albeit exceed-
ingly vast, field of research, and that was anatomy. Anything he
believed had to be tangible, unassailable. He would rather wait
several years before pronouncing final judgment. Servetus was
superficial, mercurial, his self-confidence was unbounded. He
believed, being quick-witted, that it was easy to learn anything.
He did not know the meaning of uncertainty. He had either
fixed ideas or else formed judgments in the space of a few
seconds. He was exuberant and uncannily quick. In his haste he
was capable of standing up to fight for any cause without first
assessing the strength of his adversaries.

He wrote a small book about the syrups then so fashionable
(probably following the example of Vesalius?) and in it he made
biting remarks about Rhases, Avicenna and other highly respected Arab scientists, and also about his own professors.

His fellow students may have been delighted, but the professors were not, and they found in his passionate interest in astrology an opportunity for revenge. In 1537, soon after Vesalius left
Paris, the university sued "Michel Villeneuve" for making secret
astrological predictions and for practicing magic.

This legal action was most unfortunate for Servetus. For one
thing, having already been disinherited, he had to provide his
own livelihood. The amorous fantasies of women and the cre-
dulity of merchants had, by means of his fortune telling, provided him with his daily bread. Besides this, he was sincerely
interested in astrology.

The star-studded sky, the mystical signs, had captured his imagination in Lyon. To him, working at astrology was not at all
incompatible with the medical profession. He could cite many
persuasive examples—some twenty years earlier Paracelsus had
published a book on astrology, while Rabelais, who was known
as a physician in Lyon, had edited an astrological calendar.

As "Professeur de l'Astrologie" Rabelais sold his fascinating cards with their drawings of scorpions, fish, rams, etc., for good money.

The art of magic had taken possession of Servetus' mind, and he threw himself into astrology with the same fiery enthusiasm he displayed towards anything he came across.* The worst of it was that if he were accused of using his magic powers to ruin innocent people with diabolical practices, it would not merely deprive him of a source of income and of one of the subjects which interested him the most, but it might also deprive him of his life.

The Sorbonne and the Paris police were thoroughly tired of all secret crafts, societies, heretics. They were anxious to restore order and were not very selective about their methods.

The prosecution and Servetus' defense fought without respite. Finally the law courts took the matter over, and Servetus proved lucky. It was shown that he had not indulged in any harmful practices; in fact he was even allowed to continue with his astrology. In the closing document of the case the University faculty was of all things enjoined not to persecute Villeneuve, but to love him "as a mother her own child."

After the charges had been dropped he finished his studies and received his doctor's degree entitling him to remain in Paris at the side of Gunther von Andernach, who indeed spoke as highly of him as was possible in those days. "The most gifted in all literary forms," he wrote in the foreword of one book "and unique in his knowledge of Galen."

Nonetheless, Servetus hurried from the city to prevent the dreaded chief of police from finding out about his secret past. For had he done so, the result this time would not have been

---

*As an aside one might today ask in all seriousness, is it really so ridiculous to deny to the sun, the moon and the stars some influence upon human life?

Scarlet fever epidemics appear at 12-year intervals coinciding with certain sunspots. Cerebral hemorrhages strike many people at the same instant, or at any rate on certain days cases become unusually numerous. The weather, people say. Yet is not the weather connected with the course of the moon, the position of the sun and other cosmic factors the connection among which we, in our life, have no inkling?

a discussion between the mild gentlemen of the Sorbonne and the law court about a slight academic misunderstanding; it would mean his certain end in the depths of some prison. Only a few years previously, at the very time when Calvin was urging a meeting with him, a proclamation was made that "anyone proved by two witnesses to be Lutheran would be burned at the stake without further proceedings."

Calvin himself had fled from France in vain, for he was now expelled from Geneva at the order of the Council itself, by the very men who had invited him in the first place. Calvin started once more on his wanderings, seeking a place in which he could settle.

It therefore seemed better for Servetus to quietly disappear to the countryside and await the patients who, on their creaking carts, brought not only their ulcers and stomach aches but also eggs, geese and chickens. Collecting their gold coins in a bag "Doctor Villeneuve" could look forward to making a considerable fortune.

* * *

But such a stormy spirit could not remain still.

For a few years he stayed in remote villages, then moved to the small town of Vienne in the vicinity of Lyon and there became the house physician of the local cardinal.

Servetus was enjoying the goodwill of the princes of the Church for a second time. And here amidst security, comfort and untroubled surroundings he had the time to ponder and think back to the first setback of his youth, his failure with his treatise on the Trinity.

In the patriarchal atmosphere of Vienne he could have lived in plenty. The sick liked him, the academic world recognized the merits of his "Geography of Ptolemeus," and however much the professors may have disliked his book on syrups, within a short time it was reprinted several times. Life brought him many opportunities, he had but to grasp them.

But instead of setting his own life in order after so many upheavals, he returned to the ambition of his youth, the interpretation of the Trinity. He settled down to write a book on the subject.

He had the vague feeling that he was the Archangel Michael

come down to earth! From the Revelations of Saint John, demons, cabbalistic numbers and symbols emerged and compelled him to defend his rights with grim fury. He had visions, and even his closest friends asked themselves whether he could be considered entirely sane.

During the day, after his rounds, he would prescribe purgatives and diets, but in the evenings he would leave off from such mundane matters which he regarded with a measure of contempt. In the course of writing about God, the pope and baptism, he also turned to the matter of the coursing of blood in the heart and blood vessels. To Servetus the matter was of no particular importance, the problem merely arising from the fact of his being a physician and having worked with Vesalius.

God, creator of man, was in a way participating in the human body. Was not the word "spirit" in its manifold meaning witness to this? "From the breath of air," he wrote, "God introduces the divine spirits into men in whom the life of the inspired air was innate . . . I shall call the air spirit, because in the sacred language there is no special name for air. Indeed the fact indicates that the divine breath is in the air which the spirit of the Lord fills . . ." Thus the functions of the body mixed with essentials of faith.

In the fifth chapter of his book he writes quite incidentally as an example of God's wonderful creation: "In order that you may understand, dear Reader, the complete connection between the spirit and the mind I add here an example of a Godly conception, which you will readily comprehend, however little you may be familiar with matters anatomical. Communication between the two ventricles does not take place across the tissue in the center of the heart as is generally believed, but by means of the greatest artistry through the right ventricle, after it has pumped the purified blood through towards its long trip towards the lungs. In the lungs it is transformed and turns red. From the vena arteriosa (pulmonary artery) it flows into the arteria venosa (pulmonary veins) where it combines with the air inhaled to such an extent that it is able to shed its impurities by means of exhalation. Finally it flows into the left side of the heart as a result of its dilation, where it becomes life spirit (spiritus vitalis).

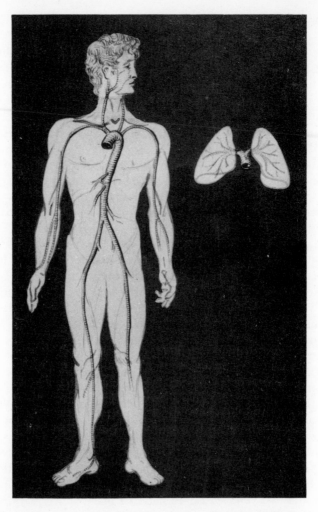

35. *The pulmonary artery supplying the relatively small lungs is the same size as the aorta which supplies blood to the entire body. (By A. Barabas)*

"That communication and transformation of the blood happens as I am telling you is shown by the many connections of the lungs beween the vena arteriosa and the arteria venosa. This is but confirmed by the conspicuous wideness of the vena arteriosa which would not have been created so wide and would

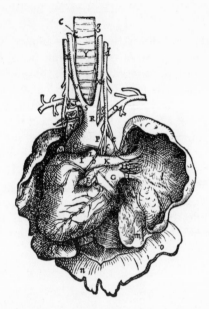

36. *Pulmonary artery (I, L, K) and aorta (P) depicted in the book of Vesalius. (By J. Calcar)*

not transport such a large amount of pure blood to the lungs if this were solely for the purpose of their nourishment.

"For the heart does not supply merely nourishment to the lungs, for in the embryo the lungs get their nourishment elsewhere . . . Therefore it must be for some other purpose that at the moment of birth the blood should proceed with such superfluity from the heart to the lungs. Also what comes back from the lungs into the heart through the arteria venosa is not simply air, but rather air mixed with blood. This mixture takes place in the lungs. The "spiritualized" blood is not turned red by the heart, but by the lungs.

"The central partition plays no role in this communication, or in the transformation of the blood, for it contains no blood-vessels and is not capable of such function, although some slight leakage is possible. The flow through the lungs takes place just as separately, between the vena arteriosa and the arteria venosa as in the liver between the vena portae and the vena cava:

this is due to the transformation of the blood, and this again takes place for the purpose of transforming the spiritus.

"If we compare these observations with those of Galen we will see that this truth was not apparent to him."

One wonders how Servetus had come to write these clear passages, the basis for which had to be direct observation. The width of the pulmonary artery, the diameter of which equals that of the aorta, evidently must have struck him during the time he spent with Vesalius. It was drawn like that in Vesalius' book, but Vesalius drew no further conclusions as did Servetus. The fact that the blood proceeding from the lungs to the heart is bright red while that going towards the lungs is bluish black can only be observed in living animals. It seems almost certain

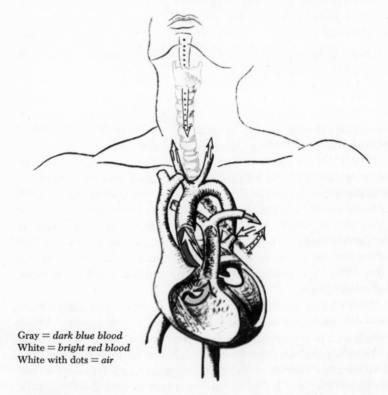

Gray = *dark blue blood*
White = *bright red blood*
White with dots = *air*

37. *The blood turns red after passage through the lungs. (By A. Barabas)*

that Servetus must have dissected live animals in Paris, for in anatomical circles this was common practice owing to the scarcity of human bodies. Quite possibly Vesalius or one of his unknown assistants may have drawn Servetus' attention to this phenomenon, or had suggested the idea to him, and he completed the observation with his own speculative logic. The essence of it was that if blood does not flow from the right ventricle into the left, then communication through the tissues of the lungs could only be imagined.

Since he corresponded with so many people he might easily have heard about the famous lecture Vesalius gave in Bologna, for merchants and various friends were constantly traveling between Italy and France. The whole question of communication between the two ventricles across the septum was, in any case, beginning to be doubted as a result of much dissecting. Also, Servetus was familiar with Berengario Carpi's remarks about the invisible holes in the septum of the human heart. The disturbing effect of such remarks by Carpi became more pronounced once Vesalius' speculations on the subject became known.

That this problem had been under discussion is confirmed by the wording used by Servetus, that the flow of blood from the right to the left ventricle does not take place across the septum "as is commonly supposed." The word "commonly" reveals that some thought differently. Quite possibly he may already have discussed this with Vesalius in Paris. At any rate, if for practical purposes the septum was solid (he did not dare to maintain its complete impenetrability), logic and truth were on his side.

He apparently was unfamiliar with the descriptions of Ibn al Nafiis, for the latter's book was never published, and only a few hand-written copies were circulated in Egypt. The Arab universities in Cordova and Toledo were no longer in existence.

Yet there may have been one source which led him to the idea that blood takes a course away from the heart which is different from the course it takes going towards the heart. As a Spaniard he, of all people, may have had easier access to this source.

Francesco de la Reina, a blacksmith and non-professional veterinarian in Zamorra, a small town on the southern slope of the Pyrenees, had a few years previously published a small book for veterinarians, in the form of dialogues (which was then the written fashion). In it the teacher instructs his student as follows:

"If you are asked in the course of blood-letting why the horse's vein on either front leg or back leg swells at the far end and not at the near end, then reply that this is quite natural... the superficial veins have the task of conducting the blood centrifugally, whereas the deep-lying ones have that of conducting it upwards (centripetally), so that the blood should flow to and from every part of the body."

The provincial blacksmith clearly pointed to that often experi-

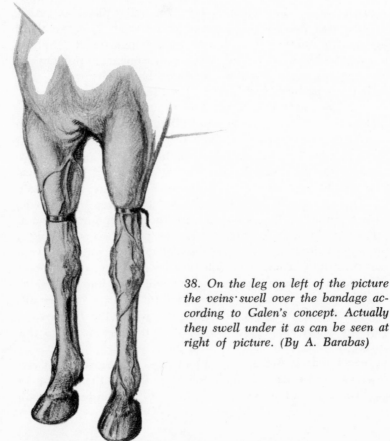

38. *On the leg on left of the picture the veins swell over the bandage according to Galen's concept. Actually they swell under it as can be seen at right of picture. (By A. Barabas)*

enced yet neglected fact that veins can only swell at the far end of a bound limb, if the filling of the vessels also occurred from the end. Had Galen been right, then the wave of blood coming from the heart would have accumulated above the binding, while beyond that point the veins should have been empty.

In Servetus' description, however, his stating that the blood in the pulmonary blood vessels does not flow in every direction but in one only was quite new. Another novel observation was that the red color of the blood is already produced during its progress across the lungs. That there was red as well as dark blue blood was of course known even to the Babylonian scientists who wrote of "night colored" and "day colored" blood. But the fact that the blood color changes consistently in the course of passage through the lungs and not, as Galen believed, in the left ventricle, was Servetus' observation. Whether he had made experiments in this field and whether in Paris or in Vienne, we do not know.

He did not describe any methods, for so far as he was concerned all this actually was mere decoration to illustrate God's wonderful creation.

* * *

Having completed his book in 1546, Servetus was afraid that he might not be able to achieve the acceptance of his views unaided and set about looking for a patron.

Naturally, the Catholic clergy could not be considered. Luther and Zwingli had died; Melanchthon, who had the sharpest wits in the entire Lutheran camp, did not like him. There were other important persons with whom he had quarreled some years previously. One man was still left who had the reputation of a great scholar and at the same time wielded considerable worldly power. This was Calvin.

After three years of exile, the Council of Geneva had recalled Calvin in 1541, and he had since become master of Geneva and the spokesman against the power of the Pope. Servetus therefore turned to him. His letters were transmitted by the Frellon brothers for whom he had worked ten years' previously.

At first Calvin replied with cool courtesy and tried to argue away this patron-seeker. But Servetus became more and more

heated in the correspondence, until finally he sent off the manuscript of his book under the "seal of secrecy." Calvin became
annoyed; the tone of his letters became increasingly severe. Was
not the very fact that Servetus had given his work the title of
"Restitutio Christianismi" provoking, when Servetus knew very
well that Calvin's own treatise was entitled "Institutio Christianismi"?

When Servetus plagued him with more and more questions (in
all he sent forty-six letters to Geneva) Calvin restrained himself, though with difficulty. "I do not actually know what it
is you want from me," he wrote. "I am much too busy to
write one man a whole book. Incidentally, the reply to your
question may be found if you like in my "Institutio." I would
not begrudge you the trouble if I only knew what your aim
was. . . I do not hate you, I do not despise you . . . but I
would have to be made of iron not to be shaken by the inso-
lence with which you rush headlong up against sober teaching."

Servetus was not intimidated or dissuaded. He wrote crush-
ingly: "I have told you repeatedly that you are on the wrong
track in approving the awful separateness of the three Godly
beings." When he saw that he had not succeeded in convincing Calvin he finally sent him the latter's own "Institutio" with ironic marginal comments.

Calvin was overcome with fury: "Servetus throws himself
upon my books and defiles them with mocking remarks, just
like a dog who bites into a stone and goes on chewing it," he
wrote to his friend Farel.

In any case Calvin was extremely busy, he had to overcome
the ever-recurring opposition of the Genevans, his infant children
died one after the other. And he was often tormented by blinding headaches.

After so much importunate officiousness he was no longer prepared to bother with Servetus. He sent the Frellon brothers a
message that he had more important things to do than to waste
his time upon such a conceited lunatic.

Servetus, seeing his correspondence was useless, suggested a
personal discussion. But when he asked for the return of his
manuscript he could not resist adding with impertinence: "But
if you seriously believe the Pope to be the Antichrist, then

you must also be convinced that the Trinity and baptism, which are parts of the papal doctrine, are the devil's dogmas."

Calvin did not even trouble to reply—nor did he return the manuscript. So far as he was concerned he regarded the wretched matter as finished.

Servetus would not rest. For him the mysterious numbers of Saint John's Revelations were real numbers. It was the Synod of Nice in 325 which had divided God's oneness into three, therefore the number 1260 in Saint John's Revelations showed that the power of the Papacy would crumble that many years later, that is in 1585. For the preparation of this event he had been chosen by God. It was probably no accident either that his name happened to be Miguel. It could be read in the Book of Daniel that "At that time shall Michael stand up, the great prince which standeth for the children of thy people." Therefore God had commissioned him to conquer the dragon (the pope).

Meanwhile news came that Rabelais had had to flee for safety while Étienne Dolet, his publisher, Servetus' old acquaintance from Lyon, had been burnt at the stake in 1546 in Paris, accused of heresy.

All this in no way lessened Servetus' determination to publish his work, yet he was aware of the danger of his assumed mission. "I know for certain that I am destined to die for this cause." But his demons were pressing him. "Woe unto me if I were not to spread the truth."

He prepared to put his plans into effect. In the outskirts of Vienne he rented a room in a non-descript house, took the printing machines there and swore the workers to secrecy. He launched the printing of the book on September 29, 1552, Saint Michael's day, his own Saint's day. One thousand copies of the seven-hundred-page book were printed, and messengers immediately took the books described as "blank paper" to the book markets of Lyon, Paris, Frankfurt and Vienna intending to undermine not only the authority of the pope, but also the power of Luther and Calvin! But he overlooked one thing: Calvin's extensive spy system.

When Calvin received a copy with the ink scarcely dry upon it, he felt himself released from the obligation to secrecy imposed by private correspondence. He had kept silent for years. But now that the dissenter attacked openly, he was obliged to step forward.

After lengthy debate and hesitation, he finally gave in to the urgings of one of his students and sent the title page of the book to Lyon. "It is about a Spaniard from Argonne", wrote the student, "whose name is Miguel Servetus but who calls himself Michel de Villeneuve and practices medicine."

A month later (in March, 1553) Servetus was summoned to be questioned by the Inquisition.

Servetus denied everything, in spite of having had the telltale letters MSV for Michael Servetus Villeneuve printed at the end of the book. He was nonetheless released.

At the same time five preachers from Geneva were languishing in the prison in Lyon, and Calvin tried to bring them spiritual comfort by letter, knowing how cases of this kind were likely to end in the hands of the Inquisition. The five were, in fact, executed. But Servetus was free! To Calvin, Servetus' release seemed to be synonymous with the spread of the latter's book, which could even shake his, Calvin's, power, since his doctrines were so criticized in it. Therefore once again a letter went from Geneva to Lyon. Again, Calvin's student was the sender . . . from the sworn enemies of the Inquisition to the Inquisition! This time, however, it contained tangible proofs: the letters of Servetus addressed to Calvin and selected parts of his manuscript.

Although the Chief Inquisitor confronted Servetus with the letters written to Calvin, he denied everything. He was Doctor Villeneuve, he claimed, not Servetus. But when handwriting tests threatened to expose him, he admitted writing the letters but pretended merely to have used the name of Servetus with whom, he emphasized, he was not to be confused, and he only did this in order to find out Calvin's views. But ". . . we have not written to each other for at least ten years. I protest before God, I protest before you, Gentlemen, I had no wish to dogmatize, nor to teach anything opposed to the Church or the Christian religion."

The inquisitor is not likely to have believed the story; at any rate Servetus gained time. All was not yet lost.

His imprisonment was unusually lenient. He was allowed to take walks in the prison yard with only light supervision. It is hard not to think of his friend the cardinal as his secret benefactor, whose very life it might have cost if Servetus, his one-time protege, were further investigated. For the two had met day after day and no one would have believed, even if it had not been true, that the cardinal knew nothing of Servetus' anti-papal efforts, let alone that he did not know the book was to be printed on his own machines.

A little later, at the beginning of April, 1553, his unknown well-wisher had a ladder placed against the wall, by means of which Servetus escaped from prison and was free once more.

But once his escape became known, the printers were arrested and a large number of book copies ready for distribution were seized in Lyon.

The Chief Inquisitor placed the parcel in the apartment of the archbishop, but first took out a copy for himself to have on hand if the heretic were caught—so he could have his sins read to him from it.

On June 17th the Inquisitor signed the final verdict. " ... Immediately upon his arrest, together with his books he is to be taken by hand-cart on market day from the gate of the Crown Prince's palace by well frequented roads to the market place of the city, thence to Charneuve square, and there be burned alive on a small fire until his body turns to ashes. This verdict to be carried out temporarily on a likeness."

That same day the verdict was carried out on the deposited books and on his likeness, and these were consumed by a slow fire.

* * *

Servetus remained in hiding for a few months. He planned to reach safety by way of Naples, we know not with what destination in mind. At any rate the first task was to get out of the oppressive French atmosphere. Where was the nearest place for him to cross the frontier? One look at the map shows that it was Calvin's city of Geneva.

It may have been fear of his pursuers or the lack of alternative route; but it is not irrational to suggest, with Servetus' personality in mind, that he was led in this particular direction by

39. *Miguel Servede (Servetus). (Copy of probably a contemporary portrait by unknown painter)*

some inexplicable attraction, as that which draws the moth into the annihilating light, "sweet play with danger" as Stefan Zweig described it, or sheer curiosity, or even swagger.

He was obviously ready for Calvin's crushing defeat, possibly fiery arguments, disputes, in the last resort even for his expulsion, but no more. For Calvin himself had written in the foreword of his "Institutio": "It is sinful to kill heretics. To destroy them with fire and iron is to deny every principle of humanity."

And in an earlier writing: "It is not Christian practice to pursue with arms those expelled from the Church and to deny them the rights of humanity."

Apparently his interrogation at the hands of the Inquisition in Lyons, which turned out to be Calvin's doing, was not sufficient warning for him. He could not have guessed that at the time of their discussion several years previously Calvin had already pronounced the sentence: "If I still have any influence in this city, I shall not suffer him to leave it alive," he wrote in those days to his friend Farel. His patience had been tried beyond endurance by Servetus' remark that "Your gospel is Godless and lacks true faith."

Servetus entered Geneva and took a room in a small hotel. But instead of staying under cover he went to church the very next day and sat close to the pulpit where Calvin himself was preaching.

Within an hour Servetus was a prisoner of the city.

Though he had lost his freedom once more, he knew that Calvin was having difficulty maintaining his power. As a foreigner, many regarded Calvin as an intruder, particularly since he took it upon himself to interfere so totally with their way of living.

Servetus' interrogation went on for days. On one occasion a member of the "Sons of Geneva", Calvin's opposition, sat in the judge's chair and Servetus felt that he had reason to feel confident, that his case would yet take a turn for the better. He behaved provocatively and his confession did not lack anti-Calvin outbursts.

It was impossible, however, to elude Calvin's vigilance. "It is probable," Calvin wrote, "that someone has been encouraging him, for he was very puffed up."

Calvin stood behind the jury and his presence discouraged anyone who might wish to side with the heretic. Soon the judge was changed. Servetus had to defend himself alone. The picture grew darker.

Every day he was led from his cell to the council room to give an account of his doctrines. The attorney-in-chief, with a copy of Servetus' book before him filled with marginal comments and underlined passages, asked one painful question after the other. How easy it is for a man to ask questions when he has recovered from the day's fatigues, sleeping on downfilled pillows and knowing that his existence among men was secure for the morrow! And how hard to step forward, deserted by everyone, into the blinding light of day from behind four murky walls, exposed to the cross fire of searching eyes, in an atmosphere of ill will!

Servetus lost weight in prison, he was tormented by abdominal cramps, he was cold, covered with lice. His resistance crumbled his logic broke down, his self-control and his reason dimmed. In his desperate situation he was no longer the self-assured scholar and arrogant disputer.

From time to time he broke out hysterically: "It is he (Calvin), the magician, who should not only be deemed guilty and judged, but expelled from the city. His property should become mine in compensation for mine which I lost because of him."

But this was merely the cry of the fear of death. In vain did the French delegation ask for him to be handed over to France, in vain did Servetus write to the Council for mercy—and a little water in which to wash. They did not listen to either plea.

On Oct. 26th, 1553, the lock creaked, but it was not the warder bringing the watery soup. The gentlemen of the Council came in silently and solemnly. One stepped forward and read: "We condemn you, Michel Servet, to be taken to Champel Square in chains, there to be burned alive and with you the manuscript of your book and the printed book, until your body becomes ashes. Let your days be ended thus, to serve as an example to others wishing to commit such a sin."

Servetus collapsed and groaned: "Misericordias! Misericordias!"

He later asked for Calvin to seek his pardon like a good Christian, possibly with the secret hope of arousing his pity. Calvin was unmoved, but tried to "convert" him. But Servetus was incapable of denying his beliefs. "Since I was unable," Calvin wrote later, "to achieve anything by persuasion or admonition, I did not wish to be wiser than my master. Following Saint Paul's rules I withdrew from the heretic who had pronounced judgment upon his own self."

The following day at eleven o'clock the verdict was read out once more before the city hall. In his chains Servetus dragged himself before the Councillors and kneeling begged for just one thing—that he should be executed by the sword instead of at the stake. He was not granted this request—unless he would deny his beliefs.

The unfortunate man would not, could not, for then, he believed, the fire of eternity would have awaited him instead of one lasting but for a few moments.

The pyre was ready, on it in a heap the guilty books which Calvin had bought and brought from all over Europe before anyone had had the chance to read them.

In his last moment of terror, Servetus cried out: "Oh God, save my soul, oh, Jesus, Son of the eternal God, have mercy upon me." He then turned to the people and asked them to pray for him.

The words, the behavior, did not seem those of a heretic. The people watched, benumbed.

Calvin's friend, Farel, to save the situation cried out in a loud voice:

"This man is a great scholar and perhaps he thought he acted righteously. Now, however, he is in the power of Satan."

The words fell emptily. No one felt any easier. Farel sensed this and thought it necessary to silence the growing feeling of pity, so added threateningly: "This can happen to any one of you!"

They put a sulphur-impregnated crown of mockery upon Servetus' head and scattered sulphur on his thin beard. Within a few seconds the fire began to crackle. Cries, groans, gasps rose from the smoke.

Up above, a window was slammed shut. Calvin did not watch the execution to its end.

* * *

Calvin consolidated his power, and the argument began which has not ceased entirely to this day, as to the justification or lack of it for his act.

In Basel Castellion pronounced: "To seek the truth and to speak it as we think it can never be a sin." Pamphlets piled up for and against, but whatever anyone's aim may have been, one name rose up on high, the name of Servetus. It became more widely known than he could ever have wished for. Calvin, for his part, did have the satisfaction that the book had disappeared from the eyes of the world. And what copies he had been unable to recover himself were burned by the Inquisition on the main square of Vienne in France.

A century and a half went by before a sodden folio emerged from the dusty shadows of an Edinburgh library. There were underlined passages and comments in the margins and among the last pages there were two sheets of paper with arguments and counter-arguments, with a signature underneath: Colladon. The title of the book was: "Restitutio Christianismi". Instead of the author's name there were only three letters: MSV. The signer of the two sheets of paper was Germain Colladon, the attorney-in-chief for Servetus' case in Geneva.

A few years later a similar book turned up in Paris with the title page, the first few pages and the table of contents missing. This was Calvin's own copy.

Only much later, when the book had become known, did a Hungarian magnate present a perfect copy to the Austrian Emperor Joseph II. This has been available ever since in the library of the University of Vienna.

It may well have been the copy of the Chief Inquisitor of Lyon.

CHAPTER SEVEN

VESALIUS' CONTEMPORARIES

■

When Vesalius entered the Emperor's service the year was 1544. The Council of Venice appointed Realdo Columbo, who had already once substituted for him, to be his successor.

With the knowledge that Vesalius had now gone for good, Columbus proceeded to pour out abuse against him with a complete lack of restraint. The mildest was that Vesalius was clumsy, provincial, and in fact a peasant. And if he wanted to prove something, he brought out arguments for his audience which quite obviously he had made up that very instant. Once, when exposing an error concerning the sutures of the skull bones he claimed that in order to clear the matter up he had examined 500 skulls. Where he had managed to obtain that many bodies he did not disclose.

He would gesticulate in a lively manner, knowing instinctively how important it was to speak approvingly about himself and disparagingly of others.

In order to achieve the greatest possible recognition he kept a record, for future reference, of the cardinals, ambassadors and other distinguished persons who were present at his lectures.

But this self-worshipping manner, this extreme self-confidence was nonetheless combined with no small talent. There must have been something attractive, even charming in this torrent of words. His lectures did not flag for an instant. In his writings the experiments came to life as in a story, his style was so varied and absorbing. The pictures changed smoothly and one saw the pig spread out and tied, heard his terror-stricken squeals and snorts and lived through every little part of the events described.

Perhaps because he was an excitable, perpetually-rushing person, he was only interested in movement and hardly at all in permanent, unchanging things. Unlike Vesalius, he was concerned not so much with the shape of things or their hardness or softness, but with the movements they made. Thus Columbus observed and dissected many more living animals than did Vesalius, which of course brought him closer to function. Although he dissected some ten to fifteen human bodies a year, he was really in his element performing experiments on living animals.

He did everything himself (he had learned this from Vesalius); the barbers had little to do. If he needed help, one Juan Valverde stood beside him, "a particularly diligent practitioner of anatomy and his well-beloved friend."

When he opened the thorax to observe the lungs the first thing which struck him was the connection between breathing and the production of sound. For who could have remained undisturbed by the constant gasping, panting and whimpering emitted by the animal cut open alive, in his pain and death throes?

He showed how wrong Aristotle had been in believing the voice to issue from the heart: together with the arteries leading to the head the illustrious Greek scholar had tied the nerves leading to the muscles of the vocal chords, so no wonder the animal had fallen silent—not because the artery was tied down, but because the nerve was injured. "It is really wonderful to think how two such slender nerves are able to perform such a beautiful function as the emission of sound. There is no one who would not wonder at it."

His assistants kept small sponges in readiness, to stem any bleeding that might occur. After so much cutting "the unfortunate, or perhaps much rather fortunate dog, privileged to give this most astounding performance for the advancement of science" finally died.

And if this was so interesting, how much more interesting he found the rhythmic continuity of the movement of the blood vessels! No matter where he opened the body, the serpentine, shining, carmine-red arteries were everywhere. If he opened the skull, the brain itself appeared to be throbbing. And if he looked to see how the heart was behaving at the same moment, he saw without doubt: the blood vessels expanded when the heart contracted.

He then made cuts into the blood vessels and heart to see what color the blood running out would be, and whether warm or cold, for Aristotle had taught that there was cold blood in the left ventricle and warm in the right.

He observed with surprise that in the left ventricle the blood, far from being cool, was distinctly warm. He was so struck with this that in writing he felt he had to present it thus: ". . . in the left ventricle you can feel for yourself that the heat is so intense that the hand cannot possibly endure it."

When he opened the blood vessels between the lungs and the left auricle he observed something even more astounding: No air whistled out of them, in spite of all Galen's teachings; but there was genuine bright red blood. Whenever he repeated his experiment he found the same thing. But if this were so, then the "spiritus vitalis," or "life blood", was not produced in the left ventricle but in the lungs, and the heart received it "almost finished." Thus the blood did not progress across the holes of the septum, but through the lungs.

Most probably, Vesalius' remarks on the septum's impenetrability confirmed, if they did not actually give rise to, his train of thought. But why should he mention Vesalius?

Columbus was very proud of his observation and returned to it repeatedly. He knew very well that this was an important discovery and would mean fame and honors for him. But he knew also that fame and honors could only come to a man through the patronage of powerful personalities; and looking over his audience he realized how important was the presence of the prior of Venice, and not to be despised were the noble presences of a Farnese, an Orsini, and other young men well supplied with relatives who were Roman cardinals and papal counselors. Thus he did not fail to remark, when removing the pups from the belly of their mother, just dead of torture: "The little puppies lie with crossed legs, that is arms, as though sending almighty God their greeting in prayer on the occasion of their creation and their entry into the world."

Such remarks were not without effect.

In 1546 Columbus went to Pisa, thence to the Vatican in 1549 at the invitation of the pope.

*   *   *

Meanwhile Vesalius travelled with the Emperor through all the cities of the South German principalities, where war was raging between Catholics and Protestants (1546-47). Between the sovereign's attacks of gout and the operations performed upon court counselors there were not many opportunities for anatomical research. Here and there, however, Vesalius still got around to working at what he liked—for a new fashion came into being in distinguished circles. Autopsies were now performed on deceased relatives to determine the cause of their deaths. It became customary to hold long discussions and play at guesswork to find whether the deceased could have lived longer if operated on in time, or in the opposite case if he had not been touched, and whether the attending physician had been "divinely" clever or criminally ignorant.

His Spanish rivals watched Vesalius closely. They tried persistently to convince the Emperor that he operated poorly, and if anyone died after an operation they tried anxiously to lay the blame on him. How ironic it was when they assured the relatives that the patient would recover shortly, while Vesalius declared that he would die within a few days—and he turned out to be right! This sort of thing merely increased the whispers and spiteful remarks about Vesalius.

In spite of such machinations in court, more and more academic experts began to recognize Vesalius. They dared to quote him next to Galen. Scientific books were dedicated to him; and in 1550 an encyclopedic calendar published biographical details about him.

At this time Vesalius was in Augsburg with the court while

the Estates of the Realm were in imperial session. Though they settled next to nothing, negotiations and parleys were endless. The session lasted nearly a year, which gave Vesalius time and tranquillity enough to prepare the second edition of his book.

Apart from some small factual matters there were others which required careful revision. For example, on page eight of the sixth chapter there was the following sentence in the first edition: "Immediately after extracting the still-beating heart together with the lungs and other viscera we took them to the

40. *Andreas Vesalius. (Attributed to J. Calcar. Courtesy of Yale University Art Gallery)*

nearest pharmacy and found a certain amount of fluid in the pericardium." Even well-intentioned people might have read this passage with surprise or amazement—were live persons cut up out of mere curiosity? And what could he expect from the Inquisition?

Vesalius thought it prudent to add a few words of explanation. "Immediately after extracting the still-beating heart together with the lungs and other viscera from the bodies of persons who had just been quartered we took them to the nearest pharmacy. . . ."

It would also have been better if, in the first edition, he had not made remarks about the greed and the morals of monks, and if he had kept his opinion of doctors and professors to himself, particularly since such vague hints had been followed by the printing of the more or less open letter about the chyna root. For his opponents were not asleep either.

His former professor in Paris, Sylvius, published a small book wih descriptions of the bones, in which he found it so hard to reconcile the facts discovered by Vesalius with the errors of Galen that he was obliged to resort to old-fashioned explanations. He wrote that either organs had changed since Galen or else the copyists had made mistakes when writing out his books. For he found the most improbable absurdities credible, but not the possibility that Galen might have been wrong. If he were to admit that, then he would have to recognize that Vesalius was right. Therefore he preferred to let the old mistakes stand. He did not mention Vesalius by name, but we know whom he meant by the despised "vesanus" (donkey) he mentions, and when he referred to Vesalius' followers he snidely called them two-legged asses.

These remarks, however, were only read by a handful of specialists, and therefore Vesalius remained firmly in his high court and scholarly position. This fact was in effect a constant and galling challenge to Sylvius' authority as the most famous professor in the University of Paris and the French king's physician.

He tried to eliminate Vesalius. He sought friends among the rivals of his hated enemy and not without success. He entered into discussions with the Spanish court physicians. Later he asked the Emperor Charles V to deal suitably with the "base creature."

But Vesalius remained and continued the revision of his book, losing no time with "the vain old slanderer." He resumed his usual careful and indefatigable work habits. He even noticed his occasional errors in punctuation. But far more than this, he had developed a great many new opinions in the eight years since his book was first published. The impenetrability of the septum had presented him with new ideas.

He no longer wrote with doubt about the small grooves on the surface of the septum. "These ridges are conspicuous, and yet so far as can be determined by perception there is not one among them which leads through the septum from the right ventricle to the left, and I know of no secret passage leading across the septum of the ventricles, although the professors of dissection mention such passages, being profoundly convinced that the blood is carried from the right ventricle into the left."

But where then did the blood go from the right ventricle?

Vesalius did not know, and evidently wished to collect further data or make experiments, for he continues: ". . . I am not a little uncertain as to the function of this part of the heart."

Three pages later, writing about the structure of the heart, he admits: "In my explanation of the construction of the heart and the function of the various parts of the heart I complied largely with Galen's teachings, not because I held these to agree with the facts in every respect, but rather because in describing the uses of certain organs and their function I am in places not sure of myself. For it is not easy to give to students an account of the septum between the ventricles of the heart . . . which is as thick and tough as the rest of the heart surrounding the left ventricle . . . I do not know how even the smallest amount of blood could possibly enter the left ventricle from the right across the septum, particularly since the heart's own blood vessels open through such very wide mouths across the entire breadth of their own ventricles."

He knew nothing of Columbus' experiments, Padua being so far away, and they had not been described in writing anywhere. As for Servetus' book, it existed then only in manuscript.

Oporinus' printers in Basel started work on Vesalius' book, but they had to leave it unfinished, not having sufficient type. Oporinus' account books bear this out. The new edition with only one-half of it printed waited for publication for four more years.

The manuscript was in Basel two years before Servetus' book was published (in 1551), but after the destruction of Servetus and his work (1553) two more years elapsed before it could finally be printed (1555). These two men would have been the most interested in each other's views on the septum and the logical consequences of these views, yet it happened that neither of them read the other's work.

When the new edition finally appeared in 1555, Vesalius was in Brussels with the Emperor. He had collected a sizeable fortune in the preceding years and now had a house built in the most distinguished street in Brussels, and it seemed as if he would continue his researches undisturbed, in prosperity and recognition as the most renowned physician in the city of his birth.

And to complete the calm which surrounded him he received the news of the death of Sylvius, his only great enemy.

                        * * *

In Rome, Columbus found his place at once and insinuated himself into the good graces of a number of influential men. One of these was Andreas Laguna, papal archivist and *comes palatinus*. This Spanish grandee was near sixty years of age and in his lifetime had reached every eminence which a physician possibly could reach. He had been in the court of the Emperor Charles when he joined the pope, having gained rich experience in various countries of Europe. He was not unfamiliar with the "French disease" or the plague, and spoke as reassuringly to the simplest of men lying ill with fever as to the wiliest diplomat. He was a wise, colorful and interesting man.

Columbus' great other friend was Michelangelo. Now a feeble old man who had done no more than a few secondary figures for the great monument to Pope Julius II, all that was left to him were the quarrels connected with the suit for damages instituted by the relatives of the long deceased Pope. He had become depressed, tortured, and only rarely did his passion for work surge up anew.

He still retained a measure of curiosity and would watch as Columbus showed him the plastics of muscles on the dead body of a small negro boy. But more and more he was readying himself for death.

Columbus knew however, that it would do no harm to be on good terms with the toothless old titan. And while he led the not too exciting life of a papal favorite, he had ample time to summarize his experiences in a book called "The Fifteen Books Written Concerning Anatomy."

In it he refers several times to the flow of blood across the lungs: "Between the ventricles there is a dividing wall. Almost everyone assumes that the blood passes from the right ventricle

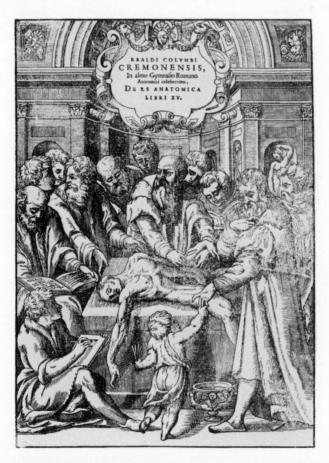

41. *Portrait of Realdo Colombo (Columbus) from the title page of his book said to be an etching by Paolo Veronese. (Courtesy of the Yale Medical Historical Library)*

into the left across this wall. . . . But they are completely wrong. For the blood is conducted to the lungs by the vena arteriosa (pulmonary artery) where it is diluted and together with air is led into the left ventricle by the arteria venalis (pulmonary veins) which no one has noticed until now, nor described in writing, although every one should take particular notice of this fact."

He emphasized several times that there was "shining, dilute and beautiful blood, like that which was meant when talking of arterial blood" not only in the left ventricle but already in the arteria venosa (pulmonary veins). A little further he adds: "Make the experiment with perseverance on animals and I urge you, oh qualified reader, to dissect live; in other words perform the experiment so as to see whether what I have said agrees with the facts, for if so you will find the arteria venalis (pulmonary veins) full of such blood and not full of air and soot."

And while he complacently wrote these lines and the pages piled up on his table to inform the world of his great discovery, the book on anatomy by his former student Juan Valverde was published.

In Valverde's 300-page book, which was full of illustrations copied from Vesalius and which dealt in such detail with bones and muscles that there were only three pages left for the heart, and not quite one page for the lungs, he described in detail the course taken by the blood from the right ventricle across the lungs towards the left ventricle. Valverde mentions Columbus as a participant in the experiments, but he gives the impression to the unsuspecting reader, ignorant of his inferior connection with Columbus, that he, Valverde, was at least equally responsible for the discovery.

Columbus took no notice of Valverde's book, although it was printed in Rome. It is hard to believe that he should have failed to see it in the windows of the booksellers' shops, or that he should not have been informed of his former assistant's success. Perhaps it may have been that Valverde wrote in Spanish and Columbus could therefore not even read the book. Or perhaps being so vain he purposely took no notice of it.

He obviously awaited the publication of his own book with excitement and there is no doubt that he pictured himself hand-

42. *Juan Valverde. (Title page of his book. By unknown master. Courtesy of the Yale Medical Historical Library.)*

ing out brand new copies to the pope, to Laguna and to Michelangelo, and imagined the reactions of his colleagues, not least among these the arrogant and harsh Vesalius.

The book was duly published in 1559—but Columbus did not live to see it.

He died a few weeks before the arrival of the first copies in Rome.

Three men had described the same thing: the course of blood from the right ventricle to the left atrium through the lung. Ibn Al Nafiis had been forgotten. Servetus and Columbus did not live to witness the reactions of their contemporaries. This was reserved for a fourth, Valverde, who had very little real part in the whole matter. But in any case it would have been useless for Valverde to pride himself unduly, for although his book preceded his master's by three years, it was Columbus' book which became famous.

Of Vesalius, whose zeal had opened such endless possibilities, who had reopened the eyes of the medical profession to the breadth of the science of anatomy, who had put into their hands experimental methods and brought to light the errors in the old theories of blood flow—of Vesalius, there was no mention whatsoever in either Servetus' book or Columbus', although both had known him personally.

Much later Columbus' description was attacked as plagiarism, for he published his discovery six years after Servetus. But then Columbus had lectured on it in Padua between 1544 and 1546, as witnessed by Valverde who heard him. And it is in fact unlikely that he had much opportunity for experimentation in Rome at the papal court after 1549.

On the other hand might not Servetus have been guilty of plagiarism? For he might easily have heard of Columbus' observations and have written about them without mentioning him.

Yet we know that Servetus sent the whole of his book to Calvin in 1546; therefore, Servetus' descriptions may well have been written earlier than Columbus' lectures. Not to mention the differences in their descriptions.

The fact remains that both observed the change in the color of the blood during its progress across the lungs which, together with the impenetrability of the septum between the ventricles, spoke for the view that the blood passed through the lungs.

The idea having cropped up in the first place presumably as a result of Vesalius' remarks about the septum, it could have occurred to both Servetus and Columbus even theoretically, without experiments. It is quite probable that they discovered the same thing independently of one another. It might have been as with many other discoveries in science: once somebody opens a gate, whoever looks through it has to notice the very same things. And the man who opened that gate for medical science at that time certainly was Vesalius.

❋ ❋ ❋

In the year 1559, when Columbus published his book, another one also appeared in Rome dealing with anatomical matters. Its author was Andrea Cesalpino, like Columbus a papal favorite. They had known each other, for Cesalpino had been the student of Columbus in Pisa and must have heard from his professor about the blood flowing through the lungs, instead of through the partition between the heart chambers.

Some 12 years later in Rome Cesalpino acquired a tremendous reputation because of his knowledge of so many topics—plants, animals, mineralogy and, chiefly, philosophy. He was known as "the pope of philosophers." Also, he was a physician and expressed his own views on medical questions.

"It is worth while," he wrote, "to give thought to the phenomenon that veins which are tied down swell beyond the binding and not before it. This can be well observed on those who are having a venesection. The binding is placed this side of the incision, not beyond it, for the veins harden beyond that point and not before the binding. This should be reversed if the movement of the blood and spirit were to proceed from the organs towards the whole of the body: conduction would be prevented, there would be no continuity beyond it and the hardening of the veins should then manifest itself this side of the binding."

Hundreds of thousands of surgeons had been cutting veins for one thousand five hundred years, until the blood flowing from these patients would have filled entire lakes. A slight headache, fever or even sneezing was considered sufficient indication. They knew exactly where to tie the arm and cut the vein, they knew the rules governing the flow of blood by heart. Scientists (Vesalius among them) wrote treatises about the way the blood came down, but no one, with the single exception of the Spanish veterinarian-smith Reina, observed the conflict between the theory and their practical experience.

What did Cesalpino deduce from his clear-sighted observation which did so much to further our understanding of the flow of blood?

Cesalpino's train of thought was as follows: When are veins cut? When a person is ill, in other words when his constitution is

ANDREA CESALPINI   *ARETINO, DOTTISSIMO*
FILOSOFO, E BOTANICO   *INSIGNE, ARCHIATRO*
DI CLEM. VIII, PRIMO   *DISCUOPRIT. DELLA*
CIRCOLAZ. DEL SANGUE   *NEL CORPO UMANO.*
nato nel MDXIX. morto in   *ROMA il dì 23 Feb. MDCIII.*
Dedicato all Ill.° Rev.° Mons.° Diodato Andrea de Conti
di Bovignano Patrizio Aretino Vescovo di S. Sepolcro &c
Preso da un Ritratto antico esistente nel Museo del Giardino Botanico di Pisa.

*43. Andrea Cesalpino. (Etching by F. Allegrini after the oil painting
of G. Zocchi. Courtesy of the Department of Anatomy, Yale University.)*

not functioning normally. In fact the cutting of the vein in itself
is an interference with normal bodily function. Therefore the
filling of the veins from the ends of the limbs obviously occurred
during periods of disease.

This explanation sounded exactly as if it had been whispered
in his ear by Erasistratus with his ancient concept of anastomoses in mind.

In his sable-trimmed coat and dazzling white collar with his well-cared-for beard and serious mien he looked exactly like a philosopher at the Vatican was expected to look. And whatever he did or taught was a model of good behavior. Even if he wished only to consult books on an innocent topic like botany he submitted these just like any others to the proper authorities, who then graciously wrote: "Permission granted to Andrea Cesalpino, doctor of the art of medicine, to keep by him and read this book. Rome, date, etc." It is therefore natural that his philosophical conceptions should not have been in conflict with the papal doctrines.

He attacked Galen, not on any tangible grounds, where he might have convinced his students and himself by pointing to a blood vessel, the heart, or some other visible object, but in the field of logical deduction.

Galen was wrong, he claimed, when he spoke of different kinds of "spiritus," for there was but one indivisible soul, the seat of which was the heart. Thence it streamed out in the form of blood into the entire body and returned to it as to its starting point. But having got this far and being a physician, he explained this theory professionally:

"The openings of the heart were fashioned by nature as to allow the blood to go from the vena cava into the right ventricle, from there into the lungs. From the lungs by way of a different entrance into the left ventricle and from there once again to the starting point of the aorta. Each valve at the beginning of the large blood vessels prevents the blood from flowing back and thus it is in constant motion from the vena cava through the heart into the lungs and the aorta."

He made no mention of Columbus' name although he knew him well, having been his pupil. Servetus' name also does not appear on the list of authors, although as a philosopher Cesalpino might have known of his writings, if only by reputation. But then it is only to be expected that he should ignore (at least offically) the work of a heretic. It seems as if he was unacquainted with Vesalius' opinion of the impenetrability of the septum between the ventricles, although the second edition of Versalius' book, in which Vesalius takes such a decided stand on this question, had been in circulation for about four years.

Cesalpino's description of the flow of blood, which seems lucid

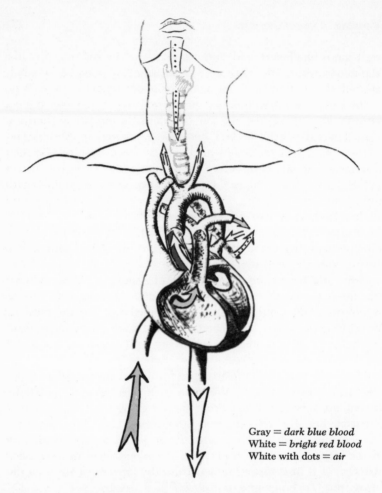

Gray = *dark blue blood*
White = *bright red blood*
White with dots = *air*

*44. "We see the blood to be induced to the heart through the veins
and then distributed to the whole body through the arteries." (Cesalpino's words, drawing by A. Barabas)*

at first glance, becomes obscured and is made difficult to grasp
by vague statements: ". . . the blood is carried from the right
ventricle to the left partly across the middle septum and partly
across the lungs."

He went one step further than Columbus and coined a sig-
nificent expression which has been used ever since: "This cir-

culation of the blood across the lungs. . . ." "Circulation," because the blood returns to the same place, the heart, from which it started.

Yet further remarks give the impression that he himself was not entirely sure of what he taught. The aorta was "larger" than the "small blood vessel" leading to the lungs. Perhaps the memory of his direct observations during his student days in Pisa had dimmed at the papal court.

We are unable to disentangle just how much he actually knew about the flow of blood. His remarks are hidden away not only in his medical writings but also in those dealing with botany and philosophy, scattered here and there in a few sentences. Nowhere do we find a comprehensive picture of his opinion on the subject. His statements form a weird succession of excellent observations and absurd mistakes. And just because he stated his views in so haphazard a manner, on problems already surrounded by confusion, his medical colleagues could not possibly notice them. He was close to the answers probably without being aware of how close he was.

* * *

It occurred to the Emperor Charles V as early as 1552, while the armies of the Emipre paced under the fortress of Metz, that he ought to abdicate.

All his life had been spent either in fruitless alliances with the French or even more fruitless wars. He had hoped that after the death of François I he might succeed in reaching an agreement with his son. This proved impossible. Charles had been unable to chase the Turks from Europe, although his brother Ferdinand had engaged them on a wide front on the outer boundaries of Hungary. As for the Protestant faith, far from diminishing after Luther's death, it was spreading still further.

It was so hard to keep the Empire together, to keep order in this vast territory spreading from Flanders to Hungary and from Milan to Madrid. As the years passed he felt himself becoming increasingly handicapped and helpless in the realization of his aims.

One morning in October, 1555, the emperor called a meeting of his counselors, governors, Knights of the Golden Fleece, and members of his family in the large hall of the palace in Brussels.

He told them of all the things he would have liked to achieve and how little he had actually managed to realize. He listed the wars in which he had taken part and the number of times he had traveled to Germany, Spain, England, Africa and elsewhere in the interests of the Empire. But now he would travel for the last time: he would renounce his German and Austrian possessions in favor of his brother Ferdinand, and the crown of Spain and the Netherlands in favor of his son Philip. He himself would retire to Spain and would refrain from participating any further in the handling of affairs.

By splitting the empire into two, he reasoned, he would insure greater tranquillity for his descendants and peoples, and in this way the long wars he had waged with so much effort and so little success could be more easily avoided. But such a hope was destined to remain a phantasy.

It is very probable that Vesalius was present at that historic moment in Brussels, together with the other courtiers, considering the Emperor's frail health and the possibility of his being taken ill as a result of the excitement. Copies of the new edition of Vesalius' book had scarcely left the press when fate gave a new twist to his destiny.

After the Emperor's departure Vesalius remained in Brussels for a time as court physician to Philip II. But in 1559 he was forced to leave the city of his birth to follow his new king to Madrid.

His name by now was known throughout Europe, and attacks against Vesalius became fainter. Particularly since the death of Sylvius he received more and more recognition, and more and more persons stood up openly in his defence in spite of fault-finders. His anatomical illustrations were imitated, his name was referred to in the universities. All this might have given Vesalius encouragement. But he lost heart in this strange country where the people looked askance at every foreigner.

There was an absence of that patience and restraint which Charles V was able, albeit with difficulty, to force upon his surroundings. Everyone who was not a Spaniard was attacked. Decrees appeared one after the other against the few scattered Moors still remaining in Spain, and this could be explained to some extent, for they were still afraid of them. But they did not stop with the Moors. Shortly afterwards they started on the Jews.

At first they accused the rich and cultivated Jews of allying themselves with the Moors and, on the strength of this, stripped them of their fortunes and jobs. And then, as usually happens when the fire is fanned by pure hatred, a general and unselective persecution began, degenerating into pogroms in several places. They viewed the Flemish, of whom there were quite a number at court, with the same dislike.

Vesalius felt uncomfortable. In addition to the linguistic difficulties which in themselves filled him with a feeling of helplessness, he could not fail to notice the suspicion and ill will which surrounded him. But he was so much in the public eye and was considered such an important court personality that his enemies could not simply have him cast aside.

It was during these oppressive days that he received a piece of writing from Padua which filled him with joyful excitement. It contained the arguments of the young professor Gabriele Fallopia, who had succeeded Columbus in the chair of anatomy in Padua. He was continuing Vesalius' work without bowing before anyone's greatness, not even Vesalius. Vesalius did not snort when the younger man described something new, not even when some of his views were held to be erroneous. True, Fallopia mentioned him in terms of the highest possible esteem: "I admire this miraculous man more than any one else," "The divine Vesalius," "The prince of anatomists." Yet apart from all this he had his own independent opinions which he was ready to defend even against his model.

Vesalius read Fallopia's little book in a few hours and three days later had already drafted his reply.

He had waited almost two decades for someone to come forward who would not refer to either Aristotle or Galen, whose road would not lie through the narrow alleyways of prejudice, who gave no heed to injured sensibilities or important connections while deceiving the world with an illusion of science, who believed in his own eyes alone and in his own sober judgement.

He took up Fallopia's treatise point by point. Nothing evaded his attention; he gave reasons, explained, replied to attacks and even noticed what Fallopia had mistakenly omitted from his

book. "I must ask you how it is that you disregarded those of
my teachings, which are numerous and quite different from
the generally accepted views, contained in my big anatomical
work in the chapter concerning the heart and the function of
its parts in which I state matters which in view of the great
number of my eminent scientific opponents would have been
worthier of your quiet scientific consideration than many others
as a result of which you collected many observations of a frequently very insignificant nature."

By that time presumably Vesalius was aware of the publication
of Columbus' book and he was particularly regretful that after
pointing out the impenetrability of the ventricle septum himself
he had not taken the next step which would have been so easy,
and that he therefore left the success of the discovery of pulmonary circulation to Columbus. His vanity was particularly
wounded by the fact that Columbus did not so much as mention him in this connection.

In the end Vesalius' reply to Fallopia became as lengthy as the
work to which he was replying. Here was someone at last who
was his equal. Subjects not yet discussed, plans not told to anyone poured forth from him to this man whom he had never seen
and of whose existence he scarcely knew a few days earlier.

He described the plan of his new book: ". . . Probably all these
things will necessitate a different kind of study, in fact according to my judgment one which will be of use in the practice of
medical science and to its rules, but also in a more general
way."

The University of Padua was brought vividly to mind: ". . . It is
not without pleasure, and with the joyful memory of that extremely pleasant life in which I took part in Italy, the real
home of talent, as a practitioner of anatomy . . . that I have
come to the end of your observations. . . ."

The Venetian ambassador, who came to say good-bye before
returning to Italy, was asked to deliver the package to Fallopia.
But it was never received. By the time the ambassador reached
home, he who might have been Vesalius' one true friend, even
at a distance, no longer lived.

While the court intriguers did their utmost to estrange the king
from Vesalius his prestige increased. They tried in vain to keep

him away from the family of Philip II, for when no one else could help, they were obliged to call in Vesalius to the sick Infante.

Even the proud professors of the University of Salamanca wished to lecture on anatomy according to his teachings.

Perhaps it was because they were far removed from Madrid and from the influence of court slander, and because they wanted to mold the University of the world's then greatest power into the first and best scientific institution, that they made way for modern teachings. The "holy inquisition" could not possibly suspect treason when trusted Catholic nobles planned the curriculum of their offspring who would spread the power of the Church throughout the world against the "Protestant pestilence." In the teaching of astronomy Euclid, Ptolemeus, Al Geber found their place, and also Copernicus. As for anatomy, this is how it was to be taught: "It is the duty of the lecturer to provide human bodies without stoppage and to perform the dissections already mentioned, but if for any reason bodies are not available, he is to read his lecture, illustrating it from the chair with the diagrams and figures of Vesalius to make what he is reading intelligible."

It was written thus in 1562 in the constitution of the Alma Mater of Salamanca, and it became law with Philip II's signature.

In spite of all this Vesalius did not feel at home among the ceremonious bows, prying cardinals, and courtiers who barely concealed their ill will.

He longed for Padua—only there would he feel free.

* * *

Vesalius, with his direct manner and sharp critical faculty could only remain secure so long as Charles V's authority supported him in the background. As soon as he was torn from his accustomed surroundings and started floundering amid the unbending fanatics of the Madrid court he was bound to meet his downfall.

No sooner had he dispatched his letter to Fallopia than he started to think of ways of escaping from his oppressive surroundings, and in this fate unexpectedly took a hand, though not in the gentlest possible manner.

One day he was summoned before the "Holy Inquisition."

Such a summons could have many different outcomes, from acquittal to death at the stake.

We do not know for certain what gave rise to his being summoned. Many versions appear in contemporary documents. Possibly a grandee who occupied a high post, a patient of his, died suddenly. Other accounts claim that it was a lady at court. At any rate Vesalius asked the deceased's family for permission to perform an autopsy to determine the cause of death.

He made a grave mistake in persuading the relatives, who were already terrified at the possibility of the patient's only being in a trance and who regarded post-mortems as permissible but a nonetheless inhuman practice, to have their beloved cut up and examined at a time when the physician did not have the necessary equipment at his disposal to enable him to differentiate between a dead person and one merely in a trance.

When he opened the chest, one of the bystanders claimed he saw the heart still moving.

It is impossible even to imagine the dumbfounded silence when the already suspicious relations heard this remark.

It is not to be wondered that the rumor was soon spread that Vesalius had dissected a living person, whether from ignorance or culpable curiosity. The charge in any case was the same: murder.

The king's physician, the court's foremost scientist, whose vagaries they had overlooked for so long, the distinguished paragon of the university of Salamanca was nothing but a common murderer!

A letter sent a year later by a well-known physician to a colleague states that the injured family added to the charge of murder that of profanity and demanded a particularly severe sentence.

Those remarks about monks so carelessly written in his first book, and probably repeated in conversations, found their revenge at last. A good friend of Vesalius claimed that he was not in the least interested in religion. But indifference was regarded as the greatest sin of all.

The Inquisition wanted to have him put to death.

It was with the greatest difficulty that the king and friends managed to have the death sentence dropped in exchange for a pilgrimage to Jerusalem.

According to another version, Vesalius vowed to make the pilgrimage if he was cured of a serious illness. But having some idea of the way Vesalius' mind worked and knowing his aims, this seems highly improbable. The more so since his financial difficulties are also mentioned, which would have necessitated his taking loans at exorbitant rates of interest from the nobles of Madrid until his return from Jerusalem. But why should the king's physician who had a house and property in Brussels be worried by petty monetary difficulties, unless he had suffered some serious financial loss which deprived him of the money accumulated from his salary and fees? It is hard not to conclude that the Inquisition confiscated what fortune he had in Madrid, which was at that time common practice in the case of a death sentence.

At the beginning of 1564 Vesalius made his way towards France with his family. He was obliged to wait two weeks at the Spanish frontier, although he would have been allowed to proceed in exchange for payment of a very inconsiderable sum. Extremely dire circumstances must well have caused Vesalius this delay.

After leaving Spain Vesalius made his way towards Venice, his wife and daughter towards Brussels.

Their separation was probably not disturbing on either side. In his letters Vesalius never makes any mention of his family, he never had a good word for his wife, and in talking of the good old days, he always had Italy in mind and the time he spent there when he was still a bachelor. As for his wife, even if she recognized her husband's worth, she cannot have been in an enviable situation beside this austere and taciturn man who, rather than enjoy the possibilities offered by the feasts and parties at court, thought of nothing but rotten bits of flesh and repulsive diseases.

In April 1564 Vesalius was in Venice. He wanted to get his task of pilgrimage over in order to occupy his old position in Padua, for the chair had remained vacant in the two years since Fallopia's death. Presumably he negotiated with the Council of Venice about his own appointment. There he would once again be able to work without obstructing spies, he would write the new book planned so long ago and would go on investigating the heart. Soon, he embarked on a ship to sail to Jerusalem, fully aware of the dangers which were by no means small.

An Italian traveler described his own experiences at sea ten years later (in 1574) in these words: "The dangers and trials I suffered were boundless and terrifying. True, the ships are large and strong, but they are so overcrowded with passengers, merchants and merchandise that there is little room left for anyone to move around in. The ordinary passengers on deck are obliged to stand all day in the broiling sun and sleep in the open in the cold of the night. On the other hand the cabins provided for the nobility and the rich are so low and narrow that a man can do little but crawl in. . . . The meat and fish is so salty that the suffering resulting from its consumption is indescribable. . . . Another difficulty, and the greatest, is the lack of water: Throughout the journey the daily ration distributed is so putrid and evil-smelling that it is impossible to endure its stench and the passengers are obliged to hold a piece of cloth before their mouth to filter the putrefaction. The liquid is distributed once a day and many do not receive even this, namely those who fail to bring a jug to put it in. Others drink up their whole ration in one gulp: The result is that many die of thirst. Still another trial stems from the various diseases contracted by the passengers who suffer a thousand torments before dying or recovering. . . . Often a large part of the passengers die, sometimes 200, sometimes 3-400 on a single ship, and it is heart-breaking to see the unfortunate bodies every day as they are thrown out to sea."

Such sufferings afflicted those passengers who undertook long ocean crossings, but those of people making "shorter" trips, lasting a few weeks, such as that before Vesalius, cannot have been much less severe. But if this was to be the price of his freedom, he undertook it without hesitation, in order to be in Padua once more as soon as possible.

We do not know whether Vesalius ever actually reached Jerusalem. Only one thing is certain, that be it before or after reaching Palestine, he reached the shores of Cyprus, apparently cast away by a storm, but exhausted, ill and helpless.

The panic-stricken fishermen who found him left him in his wet clothes, utterly at the end of his strength, thinking he had the plague.

In vain did a goldsmith from the nearby small town later take him into his care and nurse him for days—he could not be saved.

Pilgrims brought the news of his death to his wife in Brussels, together with his only remaining piece of property—his rumpled cloak.

The widow's tears, if any, were soon dried. A young noble asked for her hand in marriage and was accepted.

She probably lived more happily with him than with Vesalius.

CHAPTER EIGHT

WILLIAM HARVEY

■

In Padua they had waited hopefully for Vesalius for a while, but in the end they were obliged to look for someone else. For a few months the University looked in vain for a successor to Vesalius and Fallopia. Finally one was found and appointed, but for a limited time only, so that he should not feel too secure.

"April 10, 1565. Owing to the vacancy of the chair of surgery in our University of Padua, created by the death of the eminent Fallopia, and since such a chair is very useful and necessary for certain sciences, we have agreed to appoint the appropriate individual in the person of the excellent Hyeronimo Fabrizio de Acquapendente, who has a good grasp of and aptitude for science and particularly in view of his recent successes in the field of anatomy. And the said excellent Messer Hyeronimo, in addition to his lectures upon surgery, will also undertake the necessary dissections during the four years of his appointment, for which work we offer him a salary of 100 florins per annum with the agreement of the Signoria."

Fabricius was still a young man, twenty-eight years of age,

lively of mind and uncannily clever in all dexterous pursuits. In addition to his work as a surgeon, in which there was nothing from ear to urological surgery that he would not hesitate to attempt, he made his own instruments according to his own ideas. He gave particular attention to the binding of blood vessels which until then had scarcely been dealt with.

It became known that he was a first-rate doctor, and before long people made journeys from the most distant parts of Italy to be operated on and diagnosed by him. Thus after his four-year appointment came to an end it was extended without objection.

The year was 1571 and Venice was at the summit of its power. That year the Turkish fleet was defeated at Lepanto and there seemed nothing to hinder the growth of affluence and a life of ease.

Fabricius was made Knight of the Order of St. Mark and honorary freeman of the city of Padua. The Prince of Urbino consulted him because of a serious illness and later Fabricius' friend, the young professor Galileo, also called him when he wanted a tooth pulled, or had a fever.

But despite so much work with his medical practice, he did not forget the real purpose of his appointment: the pursuit of science. Although he was well versed in classical scientific literature he did not neglect empirical studies.

It was towards the end of the 1570's that he began to note peculiar formations on the veins while dissecting: In places small flaps hung down into the inside of the veins. They were like small sacks (usually two opposite one another) and they resembled the valves of the heart. He was very pleased, not remembering ever having read about them. He showed these to his students, accumulated new data, but did not describe them in a final writing.

Yet it came about that one of his German students was the first to draw a picture of these small sacks in a book published in the 1570's, when he returned to Germany and also became an anatomist. A year later an Italian also wrote of them. But Fabricius took no notice of it. He was slow and cautious. He had to be sure of his material and about the function of these venous sacks.

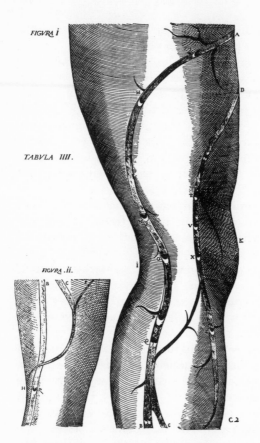

FIGVRA i

TABVLA IIII.

FIGVRA .ii.

45. *Venous valves in opened-up veins of the leg in the book of Fabricius. (Courtesy of the Yale, Medical Historical Library)*

Finally in 1601 (he was now 63 years old) he decided to publish a small book about them, for he felt he had arrived at the solution of the problem.

The little sacks stood out into the inside of the veins with their openings uppermost. They obstructed the downward flow of blood, for when they were swollen the blood could proceed no further. What was the purpose of this arrangement? It could only be that as the blood coursed towards the feet and the lower extremities as well as towards the fingers, it would burst open the walls of the veins with its weight if the small sacks did not prevent this from happening. Filled with blood, the free ends of the two sacks lying opposite one another fit together and prevented the further progress of the blood.

He made exact drawings of opened veins and pointed out that when the arm is bound these valves become visible even from the outside in the form of small protuberances.

Fabricius showed the pictures to his students, among them an Englishman named Harvey who attentively examined the diagrams and listened to what his teacher had to say.

A number of Englishmen were beginning to acquire wealth and to travel throughout Europe. The defeat of the Spanish Armada, the profits from the American colonies and the rapid growth of a powerful merchant shipping industry had greatly enriched this small country. Thus young Harvey, son of a well-to-do turkey merchant, could afford to allow himself an interest in his master's illustrations of venous valves in far distant Padua.

* * *

The world had never seen a lecture hall to equal that built in 1595 in Padua according to Professor Fabricius' design. The dissecting table was surrounded on all sides by a gallery, and the rows of seats were built one practically vertically above the other, in order that the body should be visible from any point. From above, it looked like the inside of a snail standing upside down, with the lecturer at the center, talking. The organs held up for inspection could not always be seen well, for only eight large candles flickered in the candelabra, and as many were held in hand by eight students. Although they were gigantic candles, the swaying light tended to blind, leaving the important objects in semi-darkness.

The hall was usually crowded to capacity, for according to custom not only the medical students, but the law, philosophy and theological students from nearby colleges also attended the dissections to get a glimpse of the somewhat repelling but nonetheless highly interesting secrets of the human body.

On the other hand, medical students, to whom dissections were routine, also went to hear lectures apparently unrelated to their own specialties. But what value could the laws of gravity possibly have for a future physician? When could he possibly make use of what he heard from Galileo, namely that the speed of a falling body is the same no matter what its substance, whereas

Aristotle had said that light bodies fall rapidly and heavy ones slowly?

Part of the reason was that next to Professor Fabricius, the younger Galileo was the most popular in Padua. His popularity may have been enhanced by the fact that on Sundays he often went in to Venice (only twenty miles from Padua) to drink a little at one of the casinos, to strum his lute, and on these occasions he sometimes met his students. It did his reputation no harm that he was known to live with a pretty waitress whom he did not consider it important to marry.

Of course these extra-curricular activities in themselves would not have explained why often 2000 of Padua's 4000 students would cram themselves into the lecture hall and the lobby outside to hear his lectures. The reason was that he was able to make those dry mathematical and physical laws so interesting with common examples and simple experiments that it was impossible not to be attentive.

He did little lecturing from books. To explain properties and laws of momentum, he had a wooden trough brought in. He measured the speed of the rolling ball with a sand clock, making his audience participate in the excitement of experimentation. He preferred to speak Italian rather than Latin, his words flowed on lightly—though for the foreign students this presented a slight difficulty.

* * *

Students from the most varied parts of Europe gathered together at the University of Padua. There were Germans, Poles, Englishmen, Scotchmen, Dutchmen, Spaniards. Each would maintain his national customs and there was no religious interference.

The Venetian republic was careful not to permit any sort of outside influence in its affairs, not even from the pope. The spirit was the more free since the state's chief theologian, father Paolo Sarpi, had spent several years as a prisoner of the Inquisition. Those endless months had not increased his admiration either for the methods employed by religion or for the pope.

Besides his theological duties Sarpi was interested in physics. He is said to have invented the thermometer, but since all his papers were destroyed after his death this cannot be proved.

In 1598, the year of Harvey's arrival in Padua, it happened that the Germans were blustering against Fabricius because he had dared to make jokes about their bad Italian accent when he was lecturing about the larynx and speech. (After long arguments they were finally placated, particularly when he dedicated his new work "Development of the Embryo" to the German people as a "token of friendship and esteem.")

Harvey, who proved to be Fabricius' hardest-working student, became the spokesman of the small group of Englishmen and was elected their representative. Each nationality had such deputies, and every two years they participated in the election of the new rector. They would also hold conferences during which they often rose up to rail vociferously against the professors. The students at the law college also elected Harvey to be their representative, which was no small matter, since in the life of the University the law students were considered much more distinguished than the medical students and accordingly enjoyed more authority.

Harvey entered Fabricius' institute which was then in the midst of the most intensive research and discussion. Fabricius had just collected the material for his book on the development of animals, after which he intended to summarize his findings on veinous valves. Such ventures involve a tremendous amount of reading, dissecting, thinking, and the young medical student entering this whirlpool of scientific problems naturally tends to absorb an abundance of enthusiasm and assurance at being considered worthy to participate in such important matters. Harvey, who was small compared to his strapping compatriots, with black wavy hair, and who spoke with lively gestures in a manner more Italian than English, threw himself passionately into the problems of the development of the embryo and the movement of the blood.

He frequently must have met Paolo Sarpi who was interested in the movement of the blood, the role of the valves and the movements of the heart from a mechanical and hydrodynamic standpoint. Sarpi and Fabricius endlessly discussed the possibilities of the movement of blood in the veins, and there were those who attributed a large share of the professor's work on

46. *Fabrizio d'Acquapendente (Fabricius). (Courtesy of Ciba Z. Basel, 1937, in the article of K. Zurbach)*

venous valves to Sarpi. Galileo was a friend of both men and most probably also took an occasional part in the discussions.

Harvey must often have witnessed the mathematical and physical analysis of the problem of the bloodstream from men who were not overcome by the very sound of an ancient name, who on the contrarary brought all obscurities and inaccuracies they discovered out into the open.

In these discussions Harvey evidently displayed exceptional knowledge and in fact may even have asked thought-provoking questions. He was regarded in high praise. His diploma read: "He had conducted himself so wonderfully well in the examination and had shown such skill, memory and learning that he had far surpassed even the great hopes which his examiners held for him." Though this official text was the same for everybody finishing his term in Padua, it was surely true in Harvey's case!

The moment of parting finally arrived (April 1602). He had to leave his cheerful companions and the eminent, aging Fabricius to whom he owed so much, and the vital personalities of Paolo Sarpi and Galileo. He had to return to England. His father had already spent more on him than a good turkey merchant would generally have spent on his son.

* * *

As soon as he arrived he hastened to Cambridge to have his foreign degree accepted and to obtain from the College of Physicians permission to practice medicine "in London and within seven miles of the city." And at the end of 1604, Harvey led Elizabeth Brown, whose father was previously Queen Elizabeth's house physician, to the altar. They took up residence near the city church of St. Martin's, in the immediate neighborhood of the House of Physicians and Saint Bartholomew's hospital.

Harvey was still in Cambridge when Queen Elizabeth died. Her successor, James, son of Mary Stuart of Scotland, was crowned in 1603, with the whole of London in the streets to see the coronation procession. One era was over and another beginning, and good things were expected of this new king.

But within one short year James succeeded in antagonizing both the Puritans and the Catholics and then added a further blunder to the mistakes he had already made by sending Sir Walter Raleigh, the recently feted hero, the idol of the country's youth, into the Tower.

In addition, the strangeness of his accent overshadowed the initial popularity of his Scottish customs. In spite of his intelligence he handled everything clumsily. Towards the end of his reign he was described as "The wisest fool in Christendom" by a contemporary.

Vainly did Sir Francis Bacon warn him to come to terms with the Puritans; he would not listen, although there were few people who remained indifferent to Bacon's arguments and powers of reasoning. Speaking of the formidable Bacon, Ben Jonson said: "No man ever spoke more neatly, more compressedly, more weightily, or suffered less emptiness, less idleness in what he uttered. . . His hearers could not cough or look aside from him without loss. He commanded where he spoke. . . No man had their affections more in his power. The fear of every man that heard him was lest that he should make an end."

But when neither he nor James' Scottish favorites could not help to bring James round to a wiser estimate of the situation, Bacon—not the man to cling to a problem if it was in any way uncomfortable—"retired" to philosophy, which he regarded as his true calling. For him the contacts provided by politics served only to secure the upkeep of his expensive household. He considered himself a philosopher first. And at that time (in 1605) he published his book "The Advancement of Learning", which deeply as it must have affected all those who read it, must have had a particularly great effect on young Harvey.

In this book Bacon set as his goal an accurate knowledge of nature. He called upon the King—who was so proud of his learning—to give effective support to scholars for ". . . as the secretaries and spies of princes and states bring in bills for intelligence, so you must allow the spies of nature to bring in their bills if you would not want to be ignorant of many things worthy to be known."

What he had in mind here was the importance of mathematics in science (and Harvey heard again what he had already heard from Galileo) and the importance of medical science, which is "a musical instrument of much and exquisite workmanship, easily put out of tune."

*   *   *

After entering the College of Physicians in London, Harvey still had four years to go before he could be elected a fellow. Then he would earn the right to treat patients lying in the hospital. But first, for a year and a half he was a locum tenens, and it was 1610 before he crossed the threshhold as a full-fledged physician.

Once a week he had to appear in the lobby of the hospital where he gave treatment to the poor out-patients. Beside him stood on one side the steward and on the other the nurse and the apothecary to whom he handed the required prescriptions on the spot.

He had no idea of the exciting days Galileo was living through in Rome while he was attending to his out-patients.

For about a year and a half rumor had it in Italy that Galileo had created a wonderful contraption which, if one looked into it, made distant objects seem so close as to be touchable with the outstretched hand. Magnifying instruments consisting of several lenses had been constructed around 1600 in Holland by Lippershey and Jansen, the spectacle makers. Galileo might have heard about their invention from merchants trading between Holland and Venice. He experimented with his own lenses and for three months seemed to be obsessed by the idea of bringing far-away objects into closer view.

Then one day he directed the glass at the sky. What he saw was unheard of! The moon was not a white plate, but an obvious sphere full of hills and valleys! And the Milky Way was not a light-colored ribbon, but milliards of sparkling stars!

Galileo travelled to Rome to see the pope; and the cardinals and Jesuit mathematicians declared his astronomical observations to be correct. Thus by manipulating the simple magnifying glass in certain ways (and for a long while Galileo did not reveal the secret) they discovered new worlds.

Harvey could only have learned about all this some time later, just as he absent-mindedly heard about the activities going on in Parliament not far from St. Bartholomew's hospital.

Certain revenues were under discussion, as was the King's annual income, with which members of Parliament were constantly interfering. This of course irritated the King.

But it became intolerable to the King when the case of 300 Puritan preachers was being raised to plague him. He dissolved Parliament (1611), and the breach which had threatened for some time between king and country was finally made.

Many were afraid they would be persecuted for their faith, others were distraught by the insecurity caused by the constant disputes. Fear of the future, anxiety for the family, for bread, for life itself suggested a desperate step to many—that of leaving England.

The "New England" of the distant land overseas beckoned to them, promising freedom. The wild animals, the tomahawks of the Indians, the strange country without roads or cities did not sound encouraging. But fear gave men determination. Thousands every year set sail for the colonies.

* * *

Harvey gave complete satisfaction in the performance of his duties at St. Bartholomew's hospital. In 1613 he was elected censor, which meant that with three other persons he decided who should be granted permission to practice medicine in London and its environs. By the time he was 35 he was elected fellow of the College of Physicians, and he grew every year in his colleagues' estimation. He was called upon to occupy a property consisting of two houses and a garden adjoining the hospital so he could be closer to his work. Two years later he embarked upon his lectures on surgery and anatomy as full professor.

The lectures took place in accordance with strict ritual. The attendant greeted the arrivals according to their rank, accompanied by phrases such as ". . . be pleased to attend. . .", or "Our Masters desire your company in your gown and flat cap. . ."

Harvey had to stand beside the body in his doctor's cap, white linen apron and white cotton gloves, of which there were several clean pairs on hand in case of soiling. He gestured with animation and pointed to the part in question with a small rod made of whale bone with a silver handle, while his assistant, also a physician, performed the necessary tasks.

Although the lectures were ritualistic and although Harvey had to take Galen as his main source, with frequent references to Aristotle, Harvey found ample opportunities to expound his views on the blood stream. Certain aspects of the issue had been puzzling him for some time. He had to think out a solution which would differ from that which he was expected to teach.

He was confused by all the contradictory theories, which often seemed so lacking of any proof. Some said that murky vapors left the body through the pores of the skin. But he had never seen any such thing. Another thing he found odd was the assertion that blood takes on air through the pores of the skin. But what if a person is immersed in water? How would the skin be able to take on air then?

And again, how strange was the assertion that when the arteries enlarged rhythmically with each pulse beat, this took place by their own action. But if this were so, then the arteries should suck in, unlike what one saw when one opened an artery—which showed that the artery did not suck in but pressed out: in other words, that the blood is expelled from within. Such expulsion, however, could only take place if during the period of rhythmical dilation the wall of the artery is enlarged as a result of an increase of the pressure inside the artery, the pressure deriving from quite far from the heart.

And they said that the reason the "spirit", going from the lungs into the left auricle then the left ventricle and finally into the aorta, could not flow backwards from the aorta was that the valves prevented it from so doing. Yet believing this, how was it they did not object to the passage of the murky vapors along this route, despite the closure of the valves? In fact how could the blood or the heart perform the separation of the "spirit" and the "murky vapors"? Not to mention the fact that neither was to be found in the blood vessels between the lungs and the left auricle when these were cut open.

They they spoke of pores in the septum between the ventricles of the heart. But there *were* no pores. Even if there were, how could one ventricle draw anything out of the other, when they contracted and expanded simultaneously? If the movement of blood took place across them, what would be the point of the numerous small blood vessels in the ventricles' walls supplying them with nourishment, when the blood trickling through the "little pores" would have been able to provide this nourishment?

And was it not strange that once inside the tissues, the blood should simply disappear? It was unbelievable. For even if one small artery is damaged by someone in the course of experimentation a great deal of blood runs out within minutes. Was it likely that all this should simply vanish inside the tissues? Besides which the valves of the aorta in any case did not permit any backward flow, thus the blood constantly being expelled would have strained the arteries to the point of rupture, which does not happen. Or else the blood would have to run out somewhere, which we do not see!

But where should it run? Perhaps towards the veins across the flesh in order to return to the heart?

If he cut through an artery at any point, the experimental animal bled to death—even Galen knew that. But when the animal finally died and the body was opened up, the blood was missing not only from the arteríes where he had let it out, but also from the veins.

Did it now follow from all this that the veins contained the same blood as the arteries and that all of it coursed round and round?

Harvey worked it all out, believing the blood to flow not like the tides of the sea, constantly to and fro, essentially moving in one place, as the ancients had said, but in one direction only, from the heart to the aorta, from there through the arteries to every part of the body, then finally through the veins back into the heart, always in a circle.

This seemed to be borne out by a simple experiment: if an animal had an artery tied down in its leg, the part running towards the heart filled to the bursting point and swelled the artery, while beyond the ligature not only did the artery flatten out, being empty, but the veins also, indicating that the source from which they drew their supply of blood was now closed.

Another thought which gave him pause was that if the blood intended for the veins were made in the liver from substances prepared from daily nourishment, then after reaching the heart and the rest of the body it would soon be exhausted. That the veins are not exhausted indicates that they must get their replacements elsewhere. The most obvious possibility appeared that they should get them from the arteries. Thus this also spoke for the all-around circulation of the blood.

Harvey must have given thought to all these problems over a number of years.

It may be that they occurred to him even in Padua in the course of the talks with Fabricius and Sarpi. It is also possible that he only began to ponder these incongruities in the course of his practice at St. Bartholomew's Hospital, or during his period as censor, listening to the examination candidates' mumblings; possibly their uncertainties and errors may have drawn his attention to the weak points in the teachings thousands of years old.

On the solemn occasion of his first taking possession of his chair as professor of anatomy he merely noted in his book (for his private use only) that: "It is plain from the structure of the

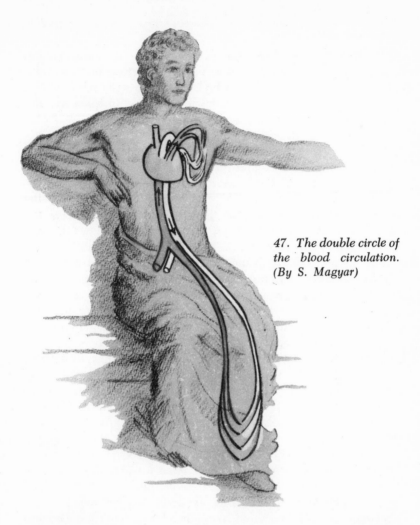

47. *The double circle of the blood circulation. (By S. Magyar)*

heart that the blood is passed continuously through the lungs to the aorta as by the two clacks of a water bellows to raise water.

"It is shown by the application of a ligature that the passage of blood is from the arteries into the veins, whence it follows that the movement of the blood is constantly in a circle, and is brought about by the beat of the heart."

The lecture was held on April 17, 1616, in the dissecting room of the College of Physicians and it is probably safe to assume that it must have occasioned amazement, confusion, and in some even scandalized shock. For it was astounding and even unthinkable that everything which had been asserted and been believed with complete confidence for centuries and was thought to have been proved repeatedly by a multitude of able scientists, should fall apart in a heap of errors.

These views were just as fantastic as those maintained by Galileo concerning the stars and their courses.

While in London people were amazed by Harvey's claims, so in Rome they were annoyed that Galileo should persist in being so obstinate as to assert that the sun was static and that the earth whirled around it at an incredible speed once a year, and on top of this revolved on its own axis once a day!

For the moment the leaders of the Inquisition did not attack Galileo, but merely warned him politely but unmistakably: Should he continue to publicize his intolerable views and refuse to resign himself to their prohibition, he would be imprisoned. But he could keep his opinions to himself so far as the inquisitors were concerned.

Those who learned of the episode regarded Galileo as a somewhat odd and obstinate eccentric. The Florentine ambassador, who had been sent to Rome with Galileo to smooth his path, wrote in the following terms to his prince: "My lord Galileo's discussions were dissolved in alchemistic smoke; the Holy Office declared that to hold on to such views constituted an apparent deviation from the Church's infallible dogmas. Thus we are reassured once more that whatever circles we may describe with our minds, we are yet standing in one place and not flying around in circles with the earth, like ants on a balloon."

Galileo was allowed to go free, but his ironic remarks and still unhumble behavior enraged his enemies. Copernicus, upon whose work Galileo had based his deductions, was put on the Index. For a long, long time no one could teach publicly without danger that the earth revolved.

In the very same month Shakespeare sat in his house in Stratford, drinking and recalling the good times with the playright Ben Jonson. But Shakespeare only lived to see the morning of that day. By evening he was dead.

Sir Walter Raleigh, Shakespeare's old friend, had just been released a few weeks previously from the Tower of London after 13 years of imprisonment. Who could have guessed that in another two years he was to be beheaded in the courtyard of the same Tower which he left behind so happily now?

The calendar of these events showed April of the year 1616. It was the year and month in which Harvey first made public his new theory of blood circulation.

✿ ✿ ✿

Although there was no doubt in Harvey's mind concerning the circular movement of the blood, much remained to be clarified. He was still uncertain of many matters.

Each heart beat occurred within such a short space of time that it was impossible to observe its details. Yet he could only explain his ever-recurring questions if he could observe the series of details which made up the movements.

He saw that one movement was not a simple contraction or dilation, but rather a rapid snakelike writhing running through the heart, followed by the next one, just as rapid, so that he was never able to observe the whole and so very significant series of consecutive details one by one.

As he watched the animal during an experiment, he found that it inhaled the air increasingly slowly and that the heart, which to begin with beat so rapidly, became sluggish, then beat only intermittently. Anyone else would have left his victim at that point and gone to seek to prove his preconceptions on a fresh animal. But he waited, watched the paralyzed heart, which gave another twitch and then stopped once more. And then again another sluggish contraction took place.

Thus Harvey was given what he wanted. A slow-motion picture of the process of the heart function. The movement which in its lightning rapidity was incomprehensible was now quite perceptible at this slow pace, not only to the eye but to the touch. He could feel the heart lose intensity; it grew soft and loose, but when it beat, it was taut and hard. And the warmth of the finger could induce a few more contractions in a heart thought to be dead, until finally it lay still and limp, with all power of movement gone.

He needed an animal in which he could observe the exact mechanical succession of the heart's movements, not only for a few minutes on the brink of its death, but for as long as he wanted. He sacrificed countless animals on the altar of his curiosity. The frog and the dog, the small thief struggling in the mousetrap, the pigeon—none escaped.

Even the fly he caught only to see, with the aid of his lens, whether it had a heart. And he found a rhythmically pulsating small tube in its abdomen which moved more or less like the heart of the larger animals. If he happened to kill a wasp he would take it and look at it through his lens, instead of merely being content that he was not stung. After rain even earthworms found their way under his magnifying glass.

He had fish, crabs and polyps brought from the fishmongers alongside the Thames, and luckily for him the sea-going vessels which tied up under London Bridge brought thousands of various kinds of mollusks.

It was fish and shrimps which served so well Harvey's purpose: Their hearts beat so sluggishly that he could observe their slow movements at his leisure. After the heart was cut out and put on the table it continued at its usual rate.

One day a salmon was brought to his table and he cut its heart into small pieces. The individual pieces continued their rhythmic dance, but if he looked close he could see that they all did but one thing: they contracted. They were unable to dilate.

So what had been taught up till then was not true, for the dilation of the heart was an optical illusion, brought about by the relaxation following upon contraction. Vesalius was wrong to make such involved deductions to explain the expansion of the heart. The truth was much simpler: The heart can only contract. The blood poured into it when it relaxed. It was the same as when the arm is drawn up: The muscles harden and shorten, and thus do their work of bending the arm. And when the muscles relax the arm is able to stretch out again. Harvey felt the same hardening in the heart of the salmon when it contracted, and when it relaxed it became soft once more.

But fish were important to him for other reasons as well.

The sluggishly beating heart sent waves of blood at regular intervals through the aorta which was dilated, but after the passage of the wave it resumed its original shape. If he tied the aorta in the middle with a strong knot, the successive waves piled up because of the ligature, the heart itself was blown up and filled to bursting with dark purple blood, while at the same time the part of the aorta beneath the ligature and the veins flattened out and emptied. Naturally, since they were not receiving blood from the aorta.

48. *Harvey's experiment with the fish heart and the bound aorta. (By A. Barabas)*

When he untied the ligature the swelling disappeared, the heart expelled the surplus blood and became as slender as before. But if he tied the thread around the main vein (inferior vena cava), the opposite took place. The section of the vein going towards the heart flattened out, the heart itself, receiving no blood, became flat, almost empty. The aorta also became flat, its normal tension decreased, for it received less and less blood from the heart and after a time none at all. But what became of all that blood? It filled the veins by way of the arteries, poured into the main vein where, unable to proceed because of the ligature, it stretched the vein to the point of rupture and distended the part of the bound vein farthest from the heart.

All this supported the correctness of his theory. The bloodstream had to go around in circles without stopping and wherever its progress was impeded an accumulation took place behind it, swelling the blood vessel.

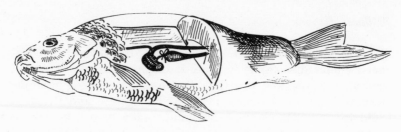

49. *Harvey's experiment with the fish heart tying the main vein.*
(By A. Barabas)

Harvey shared his feeling of triumph with his colleagues at the College of Physicians.

Some approved, others were uncertain and some made objections. This was not how Galen and Aristotle had taught the movement of blood, and for this reason alone, what Harvey said could not possibly be true. Harvey, of course, cared little for this line of argument.

There were objections, however, which gave him food for thought. One was that what was true of animals, particularly fish, was not necessarily true in humans. Another objection was that as soon as he opened the animal, especially if he cut open the blood vessels, everything changed so radically that it was not permissible to draw conclusions about the normal state from these phenomena.

And both these objections were valid. The sensitivity of animals, their resistance to the outside world, their diseases, are very different. And certainly if an organism was roughly treated it would not react normally.

Yet there are certain fundamental similarities between ourselves and animals. The bone, the muscle, the blood, serve the same purpose in the mouse and in the elephant; therefore it follows that certain laws applicable to one should be applicable to the other.

Also, each organ is only capable of fulfilling its own function: well or badly or not at all, but only its own. The eye can only see, and even if it receives a rough blow it still fulfills its predestined function—it sees sparks. The same with the ear: It hears ringing, throbbing, buzzing no matter what injuries it receives. Similarly, in whatever way the circulation of the blood may be altered, it can only proceed on its given course: faster, slower, intermittently or at a dizzying rate, but only on its own course.

But because Harvey was opposed by serious men who were recognized authorities, he went to greater lengths to give support to his theory of circulation; and although each one of his experiments proved him right, he still did not consider the time ripe enough to frame his ideas into a comprehensive whole.

* * *

In 1618 Harvey received a sealed letter from King James in which the King, "as a mark of his singular favor, granted him leave to consult with his ordinary physicians as to his Majesty's health."

He was forty years old; after this he could expect even greater popularity.

Sir Francis Bacon, the Lord Chancellor, Lord Verulam, the first dignitary of the land, also became one of his patients. He never failed to follow the fashion and would never have forgiven himself if he had not followed the king's taste.

Thus Harvey often visited the Lord Verulam to listen to his complaints (the noble lord was always greatly concerned about his health), and also to listen to his eloquent ideas about the ways in which modern science should be practiced.

Harvey observed him with suspicious criticism. What might not be hidden behind the sly, cautious and wicked glance of a man raised in the school of humiliations, and scarcely able to conceal his self-worshipping arrogance?

"It was like the eye of a viper," said Harvey. And as he listened to the elaborate talk and involved sentences dealing with the progress of science and the importance of mathematics, as if hundreds of people were listening in the chamber in Parliament, he had to smile to himself. "He writes philosophy like a lord chancellor," he noted.

For his part Bacon, while coloring the conversation with pleasantly polite witticisms, observed the quick-moving little man who had won the King's favor to such a great degree. Though confident that the good doctor was a clever man and sure that he had ingratiating ways of his own with the King, Bacon scarcely expected anything really epoch-making from Harvey.

Although Bacon's erudition was dazzlingly varied, he was not aware of some of the new discoveries. He had probably never even heard of Galileo, and Dr. Harvey had not made a lasting impression on him.

Bacon was in the middle of writing his "Novum Organum," the first book in the history of philosophy which did not deal merely with abstract matters. Until then visible objects were dealt with only insofar as they aided theoretical deductions, for example: Why was the sphere the most perfect form, or which was more important, goodness or beauty.

Bacon was not content with the life of the modest gentry which was his lot in his young days. He wanted estates, a palace, horses, rank and money, chiefly money; therefore he was greatly interested in practical matters. He claimed that the only point in devoting any time to anything was if a higher degree of comfort could be thereby achieved owing to superior knowledge acquired by research and experimentation. This was an utterly new basis for philosophic thought—very "pragmatic" and profitable, but scarcely one which Socrates or Plato would have approved.

The two men conversed and argued, both wanting the same thing, yet not understanding one another. Harvey had harbored a new idea within himself for nearly ten years but had not described any of it on paper, having no time left over from his experiments which he performed himself, each day from a new viewpoint, so it should be unassailable once he announced it. Bacon, surrounded by shelves of books, filled page after page with writing about how the true scholar should act, while he himself did none of the things he recommended to the other scholars to do.

As for King James, blunders abroad and blunders at home pulled him lower and lower in his subjects' regard. Although he detested the "ordinary" members of Parliament and despised the Puritans, he was obliged to endure questionings concerning the monopolies in spices, wines and commerce held by members of the highest nobility.

The atmosphere deteriorated steadily between the King and his subjects until finally the country no longer even spared his majesty.

In 1621 the Parliament summoned the lord chancellor to answer charges of corruption. Bacon stayed at home claiming illness and thereafter kept on postponing his appearance.

After some weeks of anxiety, hope, intrigues which led nowhere, he finally had to admit that the accusation was true.

As he himself put it—"like a broken reed" barred from all office, expelled from membership in Parliament, banned from the court for life, he was obliged to retire.

In the few years left to him he wrote historical works, a philosophical novel and a biography. Fortune obliged him to live for his vocation—or at any rate what he called his vocation.

Meanwhile Harvey faithfully visited his patients. On horseback he jogged along London's muddy streets, soaked with dishwater as well as rain, which exuded such a stench from the discarded garbage that it made people ill. His outrider walked in front of him with a torch to prevent collision with unseen objects in the pitch black night or fog. At the patient's bedside, he never failed to listen to the heart and chest with an experienced ear after performing the usual medical tasks of such a visit. The abdomen and thoracic cavity had been listened to before by doctors, but he was the first to give so much attention to listening to the heart.

On his return home he would read Galen and note the truth about the circulation of the blood confirmed—without that illustrious author really ever having realized it. "The general purpose of the valves," wrote Galen, "is to prevent the backward flow of any substances."

Of course Galen only meant the aorta and the pulmonary artery and not the valves between the auricles and ventricles, however his statement in itself suggested a one-way movement which he failed to notice. The valves in the veins also, Harvey felt sure of this, supported his new concept.

If this was so, and the blood always flowed in one direction, how much did each heartbeat actually expel into the arteries? For it had always been taught that this was a very small amount. Leonardo da Vinci was the only person to be of an opposite opinion; however, Harvey could not have known about that as

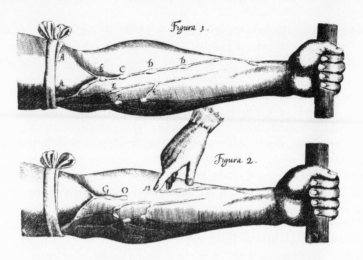

50. *Illustration in Harvey's book to show how the veins fill from the periphery.*

Leonardo's note books were not recovered in Harvey's time. If he cut open an artery, Harvey observed, it appeared that the quantity was not so very negligible, considering the abundance with which it spurted forth. This again confirmed his belief that the very same blood has to come back to its starting point anew. But it was such a novel view that Harvey feared being attacked and heavily opposed, having "mankind at large for his enemies."

Now that he was writing his book he could not leave out one of the most important arguments in support of circulation. For in his experiments with lambs, no matter how little the amount of blood expelled by single heartbeats, if all the blood was let out it amounted to no more than four pounds. The only possible explanation was that the blood was not used up entirely when reaching the ends of the arteries, as had been believed, but returned to the lungs through the veins from which it would reach the arteries again.

This was another new argument in favor of the circulation of the blood.

How erroneously Sylvius and the revered Fabricius had explained the valves inside the veins. " ... for their office is by no

51. *Harvey in the year of the publication of his book. (In possession of the Royal College of Physicians London. By unknown painter)*

means explained when we are told that it is to hinder the blood by its weight from all flowing into the inferior part, for the edges of the valves in the jugular veins hang downwards, and are so contrived that they prevent the blood from rising upwards; the valves, in a word, do not invariably look upwards, but always towards the trunks of the veins, invariably towards the seat of the heart."

No matter what ideas occurred to him concerning the movement of the blood, it was his concept alone which gave an explanation, one possibly the exact opposite of what had been believed hitherto.

He knew it would not be easy going: ". . . so much doth wont and custom become a second nature. Doctrine once sown strikes deeply its root, and respect for antiquity influences all men. . . ."

But he could not draw back. The long decades of experimentations had brought him the desired proofs. There was no other way of explaining the phenomena and the truth could no longer be withheld. "Still the die is cast, and my trust is in my love of truth and the candour of cultivated minds," he wrote in his book which, however, still lay in his desk drawer. Only a few persons knew about it.

Harvey wanted to publish his book on the Continent, in Frankfurt, in order to penetrate the old curricula more effectively and to be sure leading European scientists in the Italian universities, in Switzerland, and last but not least in Paris should be able to acquire it.

In this period the College of Physicians bestowed an even greater honor than previous ones on Doctor Harvey. They chose him "elect" (December, 1627), which meant that with seven others he examined all doctors wishing to practice medicine throughout England, not merely within the boundaries of London.

Perhaps this more secure situation prompted him to publish his book, feeling as he did the whole authority of the College of Physicians behind him

The stormy political quarrels—which had pitted the new King Charles against Parliament and England against the ambitious mercantile France of Richelieu—seemed to be abating. The King and Parliament came to an agreement in 1628. Perhaps this led Harvey to hope that a period of peaceful progress was beginning and he could defend himself undisturbed and prepare for any counterattacks. He felt the time was at last ripe to publish his book.

The manuscript had been ready for years. In the dedication he wrote the following: "I have already and repeatedly presented you, my learned friends, with my new views of the movement and function of the heart, in my anatomical lectures; but having now for nine years and more confirmed these views by multiplied demonstrations in your presence, illustrated them by arguments, and freed them from the objections of the most learned and skilful anatomists, I at length yield to the requests, I might say entreaties, of many, and here present them for general consideration in this Treatise."

The road for the manuscript was not the smoothest possible to a place as distant as Frankfurt-am-Main. Having survived the fogs and storms of the Channnel, it had to find its way by lumbering cart through the Dutch theatre of war, and the printer had to puzzle out the handwritten text, unable to discuss incomprehensible passages with the author. Reading through the book, he picked out about a page and a half of errors. Even so he was not sure of himself and felt it necessary to append at the end: "Benevolent Reader, the directors of the printer's shop ask your indulgence for the many errors in a book of such small dimensions (the whole book was only 72 folio pages) in view of the author's absence a distance of a long journey by land and water at a period so unfavorable to postal communication, and also due to the novelty of the subject to our proof readers, and the strangeness of the handwriting. . . ."

The editor was very polite. Harvey's handwriting is hard to read even when we know the words in question.

The dedication naturally was addressed to the young King: "To the Most Serene and Invincible Charles. . . ." and the opening lines were truly affectionate and must have aroused the King's feelings towards his physician: "What I have here written of the movements of the heart I am the more emboldened to present to your Majesty, according to the Custom of the present age, because nearly all things human are done after human examples and many things in a King are after the pattern of the heart. The Knowledge of his heart therefore will not be useless to a King as embracing a kind of Divine example of his functions, and it has ever been usual with men to compare small things with great."

* * *

King Charles was destined to know the meaning of heartache that very summer.

The cessation of friction between him and Parliament lasted only a few months. When the people learned that Buckingham, a successor to Bacon as Lord Chancellor, had been chosen, against the advice of Parliament, to command the fleet to be sent against France, in spite of so many disasters in the field, there were many cries of protest.

A dismissed officer stabbed the duke to death just as he was starting for Plymouth to take over his command (August 1628).

Charles thus lost his advisor and boon companion with whom he had spent the years of his youth and in whose presence he felt self-confident and purposeful, and did not stammer as badly as otherwise. He never got over this loss.

Perhaps it was Buckingham's death and the new defeat caused by the French immediately afterwards (Oct. 1628) which made him draw his old and trusted men even closer around him. He had almost given up hope of an agreement between himself and the people of the opposition. The "little doctor Harvey" came into even closer contact with the King as time went on.

Harvey's book was not an overwhelming success. Some members of the College of Physicians spoke of it with complimentary recognition. But at least one of his colleagues went on teaching the movement of the blood in the hall of barbers and surgeons for years as if he had never even heard of him, although he knew Harvey and his views very well.

He had to put up with many mocking remarks from other sources, he was called "circulator," as the attendants on quack doctors at fairs were called, for there was too frequent mention of the circular movement of the blood in his book. His practice fell off appreciably. Was it not a matter to be weighed very carefully whether to turn to a physician who was held in contempt by a number of professors and barbers of great distinction?

The apothecaries did not value his prescriptions, which was very unusual in the case of a court physician. In one case he was even sued for overlooking a fracture in one of his patients.

But the King got on very well with him. For one thing, they both loved fine painting. Charles's collection was the most famous in Europe and he even succeeded in luring Van Dyck over to his court from the continent. In addition, Harvey's first-rate knowledge of Italian and Latin, his lively manner, his extensive learning, made him a pleasant companion to the King.

From time to time Charles sent him on diplomatic missions.

In 1631 he had to accompany the Duke of Lennox, a kinsman of the King, to Spain for certain negotiations. Harvey joined the duke, in Paris.

He spent a few weeks in Paris and it is most unlikely he should not have met Jean Riolan, whose opinion he valued so highly, who had been his fellow student in Padua, and who was then lecturer in anatomy at the university.

Later, when the mission returned home, Harvey was appointed permanent court physician.

Shortly afterwards (1633) he had to make another journey with the King to Scotland.

On his return to London he was to have taken part in a witch trial as president of the delegation of experts. But he asked someone else to take his place (the surgeon who did not believe in his theory of circulation). With the other distinguished physicians they found only three of the seven accused witches guilty. Harvey's name is not among the signatures, although he is mentioned as having ordered the investigation. Evidently he and many others shrank from such tasks as the condemning of people to the water probe or other barbaric tortures. Yet to acquit all seven would not have been easy either. Not a single witch to be found among seven women? No one would have believed it.

During 1636 Harvey traveled to Europe again with the English delegation sent to Vienna for peace negotiations. The members of the mission had a lot of trouble with Harvey. He found peculiar trees and flowers he had not seen before. He juggled bits of rock in his hands and while examining them got left behind continually. The rest had to send someone back to look for him; they were irked and uneasy lest he should have fallen into the hands of robbers or been attacked by wolves.

Arriving in Nuremberg Harvey immediately wrote to a German anatomist named Hofmann, (to whom reference is made in Harvey's book,) that he would be glad to explain the theory of circulation, as he had heard that Hofmann was spreading the idea that he (Harvey) "impeached and condemned Nature of folly and error, making it (the blood) return again and again to the heart. . . ."

In the course of the public discussion that followed he succeeded in convincing his audience, but not Hofmann himself, who stubbornly defended Galen's theory on the pores between the ventricles. Harvey argued in vain. Finally he threw his scalpel on the table, turned on his heels and walked out.

Parting from the other members of the mission he left the war-torn villages and weed-covered fields of the Thirty Years' War behind him. He went to Italy to purchase paintings for his sovereign.

He had not been to Italy for 35 years, and now he was 60. Fabricius had long since died. Galileo lived as a prisoner in his own house in Florence. The Inquisition banished him there because of his recently-published book which, despite their prohibition, dared to deal, in the form of questions and answers, with the rotation of the earth.

Shortly after his return (1637) to England trouble began in Scotland, partly because the Scots were not prepared to preach according to the prayer book forced upon them by the English.

As for Charles, when the weakness of his armies against the Scots became apparent, he found himself obliged for the third time in twenty years to see his chief adviser, at that time Lord Strafford, attacked by Parliament and taken to the Tower (1640).

Each religious and political faction had its own adherents, but the people as a whole floundered uncertainly and longed for a leader who would tell them what to do. But even Cromwell declared himself with a certain restraint. "None goes so far as he who knows not whither he is going."

This uncertainty was the cause of demonstrations, street riots and rough insults. National turmoil was reflected in Parliament, which in turn was itself an arena of agitation. Tickets for parliamentary debates could only be bought for solid money. Strafford's life was at stake. What was even more important; a settlement of the decisive question of who was the stronger—King or Parliament.

The Royalist army's unsuccessful escapade decided the question. One night in May 1641 the people of London were demonstrating in front of Whitehall Palace, demanding the death of Black Tom the Tyrant (Strafford). Windows shook with the noise of shouts and the stamping of thousands of feet, until finally the

King, after hesitating nearly until dawn, put aside his fears and bowed to persuasion and gave permission for the execution.

As a counter measure the King accused the leaders of Parliament of treason and wanted to have them arrested.

Hostility between Charles and the people, a feeling which had been mounting in the forty years since Queen Elizabeth's death, came out in the open at last.

Civil war was inevitable, although the majority of people took up arms with reluctance. "We are both on a stage," wrote one to his friend in the enemy camp, "and we must play the parts allotted to us in this tragedy. Let us do this with decency and without personal animosity."

The King entrusted his two sons to Harvey. The court made its headquarters at Oxford.

Harvey was received with great ceremony, as was natural for the King's good friend and one of the most famous physicians in London—even if he diu make unorthodox theoretical statements.

While messengers and couriers came and went with the news of the imminently hoped for victory, and while the gossip and flirtations of the Royalist officers could be heard outside, Harvey received the news (1642) that his furniture had been stolen from his home, so dangerously close to the royal palace, his beloved paintings had been dragged off and those not regarded as valuable had been thrown aside and broken up.

His well-ordered collection of butterflies and chrysalises, his worms preserved in alcohol with care worthy of a museum, skeletons and preserved chicken embryos, all comprising the results of decades of collecting and the basis of his manuscript, "The Development of Animals," lay scattered and trampled in the dust.

The mass of work performed with such unfailing and enthusiastic industry was all in vain.

He learned, probably much later, in view of the troubled times, that his book had appeared in a second edition in Holland, with two letters from a colleague included in the form of a preface. In these, Jan de Waal, their writer, enthusiastically declared that Harvey was correct in his circulation theory, and he himself could support the theory on the basis of his own experiments.

He mentioned a few trifles which also spoke against the old and in support of Harvey's theories. He emphasized that he had never seen blood "boil," as the ancients had claimed. When it ran out of the heart it was warm, but certainly not boiling hot. And if his French colleague, Payan, really saw holes in the septum between the ventricles he could in no way confirm this.

All this would have pleased Harvey, since it meant a confirmation of his observations and their same interpretation by the Dutch physician. One remark, however, must have struck a severe blow.

Jan de Waal wrote that it was Paolo Sarpi who discovered the venous valves and not Fabricius, just as Paolo Sarpi had been the first to discover circulation.

Now, after a few authorities began to recognize that he was right, they were already beginning to dispute his authorship of the discovery of circulation!

The greater part of his life was over. He was now 64 and unable to witness his final triumph in the midst of war; while at the same time his reputation was under attack; it made him feel that he was in a decline.

* * *

At certain hours in Oxford people would have sought in vain for Doctor Harvey: He would go into one of the neighboring colleges and vanish into the room of one of his friends. There in the pleasantly warm room the sounds of quiet cackling might be heard from the vicinity of the fireplace. In one corner a hen sat on her eggs. Every day Harvey and his companion opened one of these to observe the progress of the embryo's development. How often he had done this in the past! Yet every time some new detail, or if nothing else a regular repetition of phenomena was confirmed from which it might be possible to infer certain natural laws.

He accumulated data for his book on development in which the formation of each organ out of invisible particles and tubes was described through to total development.

But Harvey and his friends were not able to enjoy this undisturbed peace for long.

Early one morning in April, 1646, shortly after the king, with his beard and hair trimmed, stole out of Oxford in the clothes of a servant, Cromwell's troops occupied Oxford.

Harvey moved to London to live with his brother Eliab, a turkey merchant and important member of the grocers' guild. He had always represented Harvey in financial matters and henceforward Harvey handed his affairs over to him entirely.

The years 1647-48 went by peacefully. The civil war died down and Harvey resumed work in relative tranquillity, more than ever anxious to do so because the absence of people whose company he was accustomed to depressed him.

His wife had died recently. He had no children. The King, who was his friend to some extent (Harvey had even explained circulation to him when a freshly killed deer was brought in during a hunt) had escaped to the Isle of Wight and was trying to work out ways of continuing the civil war, although Cromwell was quick to offer advantageous terms for an agreement to settle hostilities.

Harvey did not follow Charles. Though there is no documentary evidence that he was called upon to do so, it is highly probable that he was called—in view of the King's friendship and need for him. Like so many other scientific discoverers before him, however, Harvey was never interested in political matters; all he wanted was to be left in peace. He could no more be called a Royalist than a supporter of Cromwell. When one of his young students signed up in the Royalist army, he wrote to him impatiently: "Prithee leave off thy gunning and stay here."

It was now twenty years since his book had first been published. The early scorn and nicknames like "Merry Andrew" became less frequent. Jan de Waal, so popular in Leyden, helped to bring this about.

The nagging attacks by such inconsequential persons as Primrose, he ignored completely. Primrose was a practicing physician in London who had never performed a single experiment, but as early as 1630 he was agitating against Harvey. Ten years after Jan de Waal gave a detailed description of circulation in his lectures, Primrose attacked Harvey in a pamphlet. The dispute over Harvey, he wrote, could have been closed long ago and would have ceased to create any interest, if de Waal had not brought it up again. Obviously all this blood circulation business was nothing but the figment of the professor's imagination and his self-important spirit, as he wanted to see his name made famous.

Harvey took no notice of Primrose.

His book came out in several editions and the famous Descartes, court philosopher to Queen Christina of Sweden, also expressed himself on his side.

But Riolan, the most famous anatomist in France, sent Harvey a copy of his recent book in which he declared himself against the circulation of the blood. Yet how carefully Harvey had previously dealt with Riolan lest his vanity should be offended!

Riolan's book could not be ignored. His opinion was of some consequence throughout Europe. Perhaps it was due to his influence that, in Paris, Guy Patin applied to the king to have the circulation theory officially banned. In his application he wrote that it was "paradoxical, useless, erroneous, impossible, absurd and harmful."

But what arguments could Riolan bring up against circulation? What had he to show in the face of so much proof, which Harvey believed to be irrefutable?

"The blood diffused throughout the second and third area (the thoracic and abdominal cavities," wrote Riolan, "for the purpose of nutrition stays behind, does not flow back into the larger vessels unless by the sucking force caused by the absence of blood, or unless brought into motion towards the vessels by sudden alarm." There was no question of any experimental counter-evidence. A few lines further he wrote: "You see therefore how the movement of the blood has to take place without any mixing up and combining of fluids and without refuting ancient medical science."

Statements without proof, references to the Ancients—the old methods of argument.

Later Riolan went into a long explanation of the blood accumulated in the lungs during pneumonia and his "proof" ". . . this was the view held by Hippocrates. . . ." At the end of this declaration when he deals with venesection, he almost seems to lean towards the new view: "If we accept circulation, then the emptying of the lungs is more easily achieved by cutting the wall of a vessel. But if we reject it I do not see how the blood is to be sucked off." This would have been exactly what Harvey thought if Riolan had not added a few pages later, concerning the pulmonary and systemic circulatory system: "Any one accepting

52. *Jean Riolan the Younger. (Etching by A. Tardieu after the original painting in possession of the Paris Medical School. Courtesy of the Dept. of Anatomy, Yale University.)*

one system of circulation cannot deny the second." In other words if someone accepts the small circulatory system described nearly a hundred years earlier, he is obliged to admit that Harvey is right. But since Harvey cannot be right, the other circulation cannot be believed either. Thus it is preferable to maintain that Columbus was wrong too, rather than to accept Harvey's observations.

Why would Riolan not believe him? Was he too conservative? Or perhaps because it was not Riolan who had solved the riddle?

In correspondence, Harvey refuted his opponent's arguments

point by point in the most courteous terms, but when Riolan
began mentioning the "spirits" he lost his patience and wrote
with mocking irony: "As to the third generation, there are so
many and varied statements concerning the spirits that it is not
to be wondered at, if owing to the obscurity of their nature,
they are used as a general refuge by ignorance. It is generally
the half-learned who, unable to point to causes, immediately

53. *William Harvey in later years. (Copy of a bust by W. Faithorne,
which formed the frontispiece to the edition of his book on generation
published in 1653.)*

claim that something stems from the spirits and bring in spirits as the originators of everything."

Harvey probably realized he had gone further than he intended, so at the end he wrote flattering phrases: "In conclusion, Riolanus, I congratulate both myself and you. Myself for the opinions which you so brilliantly contributed to the study of circulation, and you for the scholarly, well-documented book, unequalled for conciseness and selectivity, for which I owe you the deepest gratitude. . . . This first-rate booklet will live forever and will spread the glory of your name to our descendants even when marble monuments of you have turned to dust."

This is almost too sickly to be taken seriously, although as a rule the recipient of such phrases does not notice it. One senses a mischievous, hidden irony, although perhaps there was none and it was merely a manifestation of Harvey's caution, court manners and knowledge of human nature.

His letters were still at the printers' when a committee of Parliament condemned Charles Stuart to death for treason (January 1649).

* * *

The two letters to Riolan were published, his book on development was also ready but lay at the bottom of a drawer.

Day after day he collected new data for it without intending publication. He worked for his own satisfaction.

Scientific research cannot be finished at any point, or left abandoned. When one question is answered many others appear—and this continues indefinitely. Harvey went on investigating from habit, or to kill time, for amusement, or whatever we may call this spiritual necessity which compels us to do things. The activities of decades past become a part of our being.

But apart from all this it is possible for a man to reach such a height, after years of want and hopelessness, when he is only prompted to work by his own wish, by his passion to come closer to the mysteries of nature, which reveals his smallness in the world and his greatness for having seen it.

Expecting nothing, wishing nothing, Harvey thought about the development of the liver, heart and other organs. He did not even talk of the ideas which preoccupied him.

Sometimes at night Harvey could be heard rising and pacing

back and forth. He would walk in his room barefooted, in a nightshirt reaching to the ground; after a while he would lie down again. At other times he was tormented by gout and on such occasions he would have a large tub of cold water brought in and plunge his leg into it up to the knee until the attack was over. Yet in spite of pain and sleepless nights he would be embarrassingly punctual for meals and the members of his brother Eliab's family would be covered in confusion coming in to luncheon, finding him sitting there at the table alone. After all, he *was* the King's physician.

During the day Harvey was somewhat vague and taciturn. He only became more communicative during the hours he spent drinking steaming coffee, a great delicacy at that time, with his brother Eliab.

The years went by monotonously until Dr. Ent, a young physician with whom he had become friendly during his Roman journey, visited him during the Christmas of 1650.

He found the seventy-two-year-old Harvey in the midst of his investigations. He asked if all was well with him, to which Harvey replied: "How can it be, whilst the Commonwealth is full of distractions, and I myself still in the open sea. And truly, did I not find solace in my studies, and a balm for my spirit in the memory of my observations of former years, I should feel little desire for longer life. But so it has been, that this life of obscurity, this vacation from public business, which causes tedium and disgust to so many, has proved a sovereign remedy to me."

Dr. Ent drew the talk to the subject of his researches. When they had warmed up to the subject Ent ventured to suggest that the world of science would welcome his new findings.

Harvey smiled: "And would you be the man who should recommend me to quit the peaceful haven where I now pass my life and launch again upon the faithless sea? You know full well what a storm my former lucubrations raised. Much better is it oftentimes to grow wise at home and in private, than by publishing what you have amassed with infinite labour, to stir up tempests that may rob you of peace and quiet for the rest of your days."

Objections were in vain. He did not wish to hear of undertaking the cares involved in publishing a book.

After a long argument, however, he did finally consent to hand over his "Treatise on Development" on condition that Ent would see to its publication or would do with it what he wanted.

Yet there was much important material in the book, though of course also material which he rightly thought would not be accepted without question.

Every word, every sentence was written on the basis of twenty to thirty years' experience and thought.

How careful he was! How many experiments, control experiments, sleepless hours; how many inward discussions. resulting from doubts in his own data; the checking and resultant slowness and what an incredible, in fact exaggerated amount of patience lay in this book which he gave up so reluctantly to the public.

" . . . Whilst others produce their trifles and emptiness with much ado, their messes twice, aye, an hundred times heated up, our Harvey should set so little store by his admirable observations. . ." Ent wrote in his letter to the College of Physicians.

The book appeared in 1651, while in the meantime Harvey continued with his circulation experiments, for there were still those who disbelieved and talked about the pores between the ventricles.

He thought that if he were to inject water into the right ventricle after tying all the blood vessels proceeding to and from the heart, the water should penetrate into the left ventricle across the pores, if these existed. If they did not, the water could not leave in any direction except through the lungs.

On one occasion the body of a hanged highwayman was brought to the institute of anatomy in London from the place of execution.

Harvey proceeded as he had planned. Only one blood vessel was allowed free connection with the outside—this was the inferior vena cava—into which he inserted a tube which in turn was attached to a cow's bladder filled with water. He could press as hard as he liked. The right ventricle and auricle expanded to the point of rupture, but no water trickled through into the left ventricle. Then he untied the ligature from the pulmonary artery: The water flowed freely across the lungs into the pulmonary veins, from there across the left auricle into the left ventricle and out, through the hole he had cut into it.

Harvey never made this public among the "general community of scholars," but described it in a private letter to a London colleague.

His correspondence spread to all of civilized Europe from Italy to the Low Countries. His opinion was sought in distant lands on all kinds of subjects ranging from literary works to medical problems. And he obligingly replied to these letters, knowing he would not have to do so for long.

He sorted out everything around him.

He gave thought to each member of his family. As for his beloved College of Physicians, to whom years earlier he had already presented his library, he now bequeathed them an estate.

He awaited death without fear.

". . . for I now consider myself entitled to my discharge from duty," he wrote to a Dutch physician in 1657.

He was right. A few months later he died.

CHAPTER NINE

MARCELLO MALPIGHI

■

Anyone wishing to reach Rome in the 1630's went by wobbly coach or on horseback and took the road across Ferrara towards the Dukedom of Tuscany and through the small estates around Bologna.

They made wine in this area and grew market gardens; flocks of sheep grazed peacefully on the sides of the hills. But the apparent tranquillity of the region was deceptive. A great deal of bitterness had accumulated between many families as the result of quarrels and feuds which had been nurtured for generations.

Two such families in the vicinity of Bologna were the Sbaraglis and the Malpighis.

There is no record of the initial cause of their hostility. Being farmers, they may have begun their quarrel over such an insignificant question as who had a better fruit crop in a given year or who fattened his geese more effectively. Whatever the origin, each family transmitted its hatred of the other to its children and endeavored to bring them up to be more successful than their rivals.

Thus the Malpighis sent the scion of the family, Marcello, to the university in nearby Bologna at the age of seventeen, and planned to make a physician out of him (1645).

He was an industrious, quiet boy and his teachers were genuinely sorry when, after the sudden death of his parents, he had to leave his studies in his fourth year to take over the management of their land.

He was twenty-one and his small brothers' and sisters' daily bread depended on his efforts.

For a year he managed to combine digging and watering with the sale of his products, listening meanwhile to the gossip of his well-wishers concerning the Sbaragli. But he could not endure country life for long, with the constant dissatisfaction with the weather and haggling with merchants. He left his small brothers and sisters in good hands and returned to Bologna.

Later, when the professor of anatomy, Massari, collected the nine best students (he named them "Coro" after the nine muses who lived and died for learning, as they did), Marcello was among them.

A huge dissecting room in one of the university's buildings was at the disposal of the medical students, but Professor Massari put his "chorus" in his home. This was an old Bolognese custom dating back to the days when professors received no pay and made their living from private tuition. Although the need for this had passed, it was thought more pleasant to discuss problems in a friendlier atmosphere with these chosen students.

Marcello not only learned everything which was formally required, he also observed in nature what he learned from books, constantly comparing the written chapter with his own experiences. If experience and book learning did not agree, he said so. His straightforward character required this. Such a candidness, however, did not make him popular with certain professors.

Although the ancients were no longer universally considered infallible, modern ideas were still looked upon with suspicion in many quarters. People were beginning to feel there was something wrong with science — everything had become uncertain, there were altogether too many new theories. If they gave way in the smallest matters of detail, they would soon find that the latest views had left even less of the old ones standing. Therefore it was often considered best to stick strictly to the time-honored explanations of things.

When Malpighi submitted his doctor's thesis, in which he made condemning remarks about Galen and the great Arab physicians Avicenna and Rhases, the thesis was not accepted. At the second attempt he fared no better, although he had modified the text considerably.

When there was nothing left which could be considered offensive, the thesis was finally accepted. In fact, it had been somewhat embarrassing to twice fail the most brilliant student. The other students were in sympathy with Malpighi—they knew that the reason for his failures certainly was not the poor opinion held of the candidate's abilities.

However, Malpighi was not to rejoice for long. Some of the professors were not reconciled to the fact that the tranquillity of one of Europe's most ancient universities should be disturbed by an inquisitive, doubting doctor who harbored suspicions against the ancent philosophers.

They succeeded in having his diploma taken away from him. He was only able to get it back after a lengthy struggle in which Massari must have given him secret support.

He finally won and could have started practicing as some of the students of his year had done. But he could not bring himself to listen to the patients' complaints, particularly since he had little interest in surgery, which represented the practitioner's chief source of revenue.

No one was, and is, so admired, respected and well-rewarded as he who sheds our blood, or at least involves us in danger.

However, there were plenty of others much better equipped to take off fingernails, or cut open abcesses.

Malpighi preferred to browse around Professor Massari's house and it is quite probable that he was not attracted to it solely by theoretical considerations.

While he was at work with Massari on serious matters, the comings and goings of the old man's daughter Francesca proved an added stimulation.

He married her a year later, after obtaining his diploma (1654).

His reputation for industry and learning was not kept a secret for long, Massari saw to that.

Two years later he was appointed lecturer at the University. He was still followed by derogatory remarks and annoyances at every step; for a time his lectures were even stopped.

Could they possibly endure the shame of allowing this man, who spoke so insolently of the old theories, to earn the right to wear the scarlet gown reaching to the ankles and the long pointed cap hanging down to the shoulders and to wear the elbow length gloves, as professors famous hundreds of years earlier had done?

Malpighi's position was very uncertain. Always forced into a defensive position he never knew when or how the attack would come, an attack made for the sole purpose of showing him that no one knew better than the ancients. To pass judgment upon them was conceited, wicked and dangerous.

After these experiences, Malpighi accepted the invitation of the Grand Duke of Tuscany to the University of Pisa (1656) which was not ancient and not nearly so august, but which promised better understanding.

* * *

The change proved to be for the better.

He soon made the acquaintance of his new colleagues, one of whose learning, ideas and new methods particularly impressed him. This was Borelli, the professor of mathematics.

Borelli had been a student of Galileo and regarded him as his ideal. It was not so long ago, in the house in Florence designated for him by Pope Urban instead of prison, that the ancient master had been teaching a small group of students how impossible it was to discover anything new without first measuring everything for size, weight and motion.

Like everyone else who had been close to the old warrior, Borelli had taken this methodology to heart and tried to pass it on to succeeding generations of students. At ease in Borelli's company, and in the absence of Massari, Malpighi accepted Borelli as a master to whom he could turn for advice. Thus they often worked together.

Whenever possible, Borelli smoothed Malpighi's path, though this was by no means in keeping with his character, which was often violent and hostile. But in Malpighi he found a gentle, reserved friend, who would stand aside rather than get involved in an argument. It thus happened that he was the only man to whom Borelli would willingly listen — sometimes, anyway.

During this period Malpighi gave considerable thought to the movements of the heart. Although Harvey had described these fairly exactly, it would still have been interesting to know the position of the various muscles and bundles of fibres. If the fresh heart, tough and elastic, was pulled and stretched, it eventually tore as a result of such treatment and the muscle fibers were broken. Thus it was impossible to get an idea of the construction of the whole heart's muscle fibers.

Malpighi boiled the heart until it became quite soft. The fibers then separated at the least touch, they could be pulled apart with the fingers, as if untwisting thread. By this simple means he made an interesting discovery. Although the muscle of the heart appeared to be composed of three kinds of fibers, vertical, horizontal and oblique, these were all connected to each other, and it was their spiral arrangement which caused the error in identification.

Malpighi often discussed these experiments with Borelli. As usually happens when men of similar academic training discuss matters, after a while each thinks he was the first to broach the vital question. In addition to this legitimate confusion is the inevitable element of egoism, all of which makes it often difficult indeed to judge whose brain child a discovery really is. Borelli was not by nature generous or even just when it came to advantages to himself, even with his best friend. Years later he spoke knowingly of the spiral descent of the heart muscle fibers as if he had made the original observation.

Malpighi discovered something else in Pisa too. It was there that he first looked into a strange instrument he had never seen in Bologna. It was a small table, standing on its side, its surface vertical. Opposite was a tube. When one looked through it the smallest speck of dust appeared at least a hundred times larger than it did to the naked eye.

At the fairs it was considered exciting to be allowed to look into such an instrument for a few coins. Huge monsters could be seen, with dreadful hairy legs and terrifying head. When

the viewer was thoroughly petrified it turned out that the mon-
ster was nothing but an ordinary flea. These were called "flea
microscopes."

But there were finer instruments with stronger magnifying
power. Lippershey and Jansen, then Galileo, were the first to
make these when working on telescopes. Malpighi managed
to secure one for himself.

He began to bring pieces of animals to his table. On the outside of the kidneys there were protruberances the size of colored pinheads. With the naked eye these were totally invisible.
Nerves were tied together with threads the thickness of string.

But he was unable to look for long.

The surroundings of Pisa were full of swamps, and Malpighi
suffered a great deal from the oppressive, humid air. He often
caught fever and had to take to his bed. Sometimes he was
tormented by palpitations and cold sweat.

The small annoyances and insults suffered in Bologna ap-
peared distant and childishly exaggerated from his sick bed.
The thought of dry fresh air seemed very tempting, as did
Massari's kind and understanding counsel.

He packed his few clothes, his microscope, notes and a bun-
dle of study plans and returned to Bologna.

* * *

Malpighi was primarily interested in those internal organs
which were transparent. For example, the double layer of
peritoneum, (the membrane lining the abdominal cavity) at-
taching the intestines to the spine. It was thin, hardly perceptible to the touch, smooth, shining and mirrorlike, yet transparent as glass. In fact it might even frequently be overlooked
if it were not for the arteries running into it in the form of
swollen small red tubes, separating into ever finer branches the
further they went from their starting point. These swelled up with
each heart beat while the somewhat darker veins running alongside remained immobile.

If he cut up a frog and spread out the peritoneum under the
microscope, he could see branches of blood vessels so fine that
they were not even suspected when looked at with unaided eye.
There was a network there of tiny blood vessels which had no
ends and ran on uninterrupted.

Later he concentrated on the lungs. But the situation here was more difficult since he could not see through a lung. It needed to be prepared in some way, so as to prevent the blood inside it from obscuring vision.

He cut a small piece off the edge of a dog's lung, hoping it would be thin enough for a light to shine through it. This method, however, did not prove suitable; he saw a great many globules between the intricately winding blood vessels, with thin threads running in between, which he took to be nerves. Hard as he looked, he could get no further. He had to start somewhere else. He tried compressing the lung. This emptied the small air-filled globules, leaving only the network of blood vessels which could be seen quite clearly if the rays of the sun fell on them obliquely.

But what would happen if he were to pump something else into the vessels besides blood? They would stand out even more vividly. How could this be achieved?

He cut one of the arteries, blew into it violently and then tied it. He found it came right up in relief, like branches of a tree. But what substance was there which would fill the arteries visibly? He tried mercury, injecting it into the artery, and its branches shone silvery white in the sunlght. It was beautful and spec-tacular. All the small branches looked like silver antlers.

But he thought incessantly about how the blood went on from there. "Perhaps," he wrote to Borelli, "these blood vessels open into each other at their ends or elsewhere, so that the blood is adsorbed through an uninterrupted path of veins, or else all of them open into the lungs proper in the same fashion. This dilemma has been tormenting me without respite and I have been working more and more, albeit uselessly, on its solution by means of injections of air and different staining solutions."

He sent almost daily accounts of his observations to Borelli.

He tried to dye water black with India ink to see where it went from the blood vessels already observed, but this method did not work out. The black stream branched out up to a certain point, every branch could be followed exactly, but after that it broke through in various places and the black fluid ran out. Large pools accumulated which hid everything. The same thing occurred with mercury.

Yet the answer to the thousand-year-old question had to be there: How does the artery communicate with the vein? No one denied such a connection, and had never done so, even before the circulation of the blood had ever been suspected.

Erasistratus himself had declared that veins and arteries joined up, and Cesalpino, in his usual negligent style, had written remarks about blood vessels which "do not end but rather carry on." But what exactly he had in mind when he wrote this, we do not know.

When Harvey proved the circulation of the blood in so many different and convincing ways, he found himself confronted by this question, too. But he also could only approach the mystery with conjectures. ". . . Either there is connection between the vessels," he wrote, "or else there must be pores allowing the passage of blood in the flesh and harder tissues." And he went on somewhat helplessly: "So far no one has brought to light anything valid concerning the connections between veins and arteries, and where and how and by what means they are present."

The experiments Harvey thought out for the solution of this problem were the basis for his final views on the subject. In his letter to Riolan written some twelve years previously, he wrote: "Neither in the liver, spleen, lungs, kidneys, nor any other viscus, is such a thing as a connection to be seen, and by boiling I have rendered the tissues of these organs so friable that it could be shaken like dust from the fibres or picked away with a needle, until I could trace every capillary filament distinctly. I can, therefore, boldly affirm that there is neither any anastomosis of the vena portae with the cava, of the arteries with the veins, nor of the capillary ramifications of the biliary ducts, which can be traced through the entire liver, with the veins."

This clearly supported the view that the blood vessels ended up blindly among the tissues, where the blood disappeared like spring water lost in sand, to be gathered up again by the veins like underground water.

Malpighi knew all this, but he did not see the ends of the vessels, the point at which they were supposed to end according to Harvey. Yet with his microscope he certainly should have been able to find them.

Since he could get no further with dog lungs, he continued with other animals whose lungs were smaller and more readily accessible. He returned to the frog. Once an idea took hold of him he would not rest until he found the solution. Although he never showed impatience, his quiet was by no means a sign of slowness or indolence.

The frog's lungs at first glance looked spotty and full of small patches like the skin of a whale. The lungs themselves appeared to consist of small globules separated from each other by partitions.

Blood vessels entered between the partitions of the small chambers and seemed to vanish there. If, however, Malpighi slid the still living frog under his microscope he observed something very strange. The vessels branched out in all directions in the partitions and with each heart beat he could see the

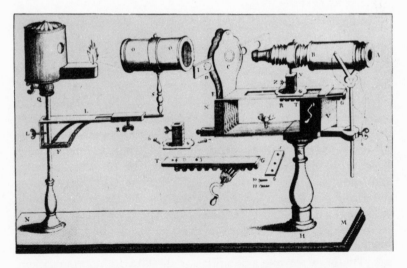

54. *Microscope of a contemporary of Malpighi. (By J. Zahn. Courtesy of Ciba Z. 1947, Basel, from the article of E. Hintzsch.)*

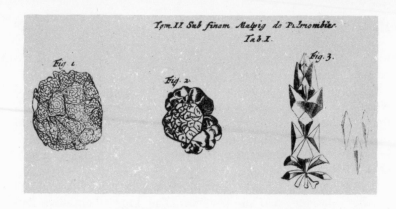

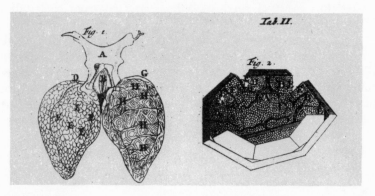

55. *Frog's lungs as seen by Malpighi under his microscope. (Drawing by Malpighi.)*

coursing of the blood very well. Following the branches more closely in a direction opposite to that of the blood, he found he was looking at arteries. If on the other hand he followed the direction of the movement of the blood, the branches became thin and the blood lost its original color. It went on twisting and turning but in a paler color until it finally reached small tubes which turned out to be veins.

He thought that the blood "opens into an empty space and is directed by the network of partitions until collected into open vessels. The basis for this assumption is the labyrinthine movement of the blood in all directions as well as its channeling again at a certain point."

But he was still not sure.

* * *

Continuing his experiments he tied the blood vessels running fanwise towards the lungs, then cutting the lungs out of the frog, hung them up in a well-aired place. In a few days they dried out. He held them up towards the oblique rays of the setting sun, holding a single lens "flea microscope" before him. He saw what he expected: The blood, though dried up, shone through the blood vessels in a red-tinged, shining network. He immediately proceeded to sit down to his ordinary double-lens microscope to follow the curving course of the vessels by lamp light.

"It is no longer tissue showing pin points," he wrote to Borelli, " . . . one can see small vessels shaped like rings and the expanse of the small vessels, branching out from veins and arteries, is such that they no longer form a part of one vessel's system, but look like a network formed by the lengthening of two blood-vessels . . . Hence it became easily perceptible that the blood courses through a winding network and not by pouring into an empty space, moves constantly through small tubes and is distributed by the manifold curves and branches of the blood vessels."

As he wrote his account, he lived once again through the moment of discovery, the wonder of which he felt sure Borelli would also be bound to feel, and he was unable to contain his joy in cold professional language, although his words held humility, wonder and triumph. "By using the same light conditions and instruments, you will observe the movement of the blood through the vessels as mentioned earlier, and using different degrees of light you yourself will discover other things there which cannot even be described with the pen."

But then he began to have doubts.

Supposing this were only so in frog lungs? Was it so certain that higher organisms are not constituted differently?

Lengthy examination followed; he knew now what it was he had to find. Unfortunately, in larger animals it was more difficult to see the network of vessels with the technique he used. But finally "taking into account the simplicity employed by nature in her creation," he came to accept the hypothesis that since the frog lung resembled that of the larger animals and humans in so many respects, not only in the shape of the small globules and the ringlike formation of the blood vessels, but in its function, the small details of its construction were bound to be similar also.

Thus there were netlike small tubes in the lungs which connected the blood vessels. They did not end up blind, as Harvey had believed. But what of other organs?

Just because something is made in a certain way in one or two organs it is not certain that the same will be true in the rest.

The simplest thing would have been to examine other organs. But their construction set up certain limitations. It was impossible to put a light through a massive organ, and therefore the course of the channels winding around in its interior had to remain hidden.

He had to find a tissue which was narrow, could be lighted through satisfactorily and could be observed without lengthy preparation, free from any necessary rough handling.

As he examined his pinned-down frog point by point, his eye paused. The full bladder shone in the lamplight like a miniature garden lantern, showing the fine lines of the winding vessels. Under his microscope he saw the same thing as in the peritoneum and the lungs, the scarcely followable threads of increasingly slender blood vessels, which then were collected again in bunches and formed veins. In all of them blood coursed slowly.

Thus nature had found the same solution in the lungs, peritoneum and bladder: The network of arteries dispersed, only to be reunited as veins. Not a drop of blood, not a single small pool of blood broke up this system, the blood flowed only in small tubes, no matter how small these might be.

What of the other organs, those which he was unable to examine?

He felt he had earned the right to draw conclusions concerning these, also on the basis of experience and observation of similarly contrived systems.

"From all this," he wrote to Borelli, "the question of the union of blood vessels and anastomosis can readily be solved in a perfectly acceptable manner. For if in one case nature wanted the blood inside the vessels and united the ends of the vessels into a network, it is probable that the vessel-endings in other places are also connected by means of their opening into each other."

He sent both letters off to Pisa where they became the subject of discussion.

* * *

The letter about the lungs soon started up a fairly serious argument between him and Borelli.

For Malpighi had started to doubt what until then had never been questioned by anyone from Erasistratus to Harvey, namely that the air breathed into the lungs really served the purpose of cooling the blood.

Malpighi expressed the view that in his opinion the role of air was to change the blood in some way, for some kind of fermentation process, but certainly not to cool it. Borelli did not believe this and enumerated counter-arguments which failed to convince Malpighi. Their dispute branched further and further away from its starting point, until after a time they were discussing whether the frog could breathe with its mouth open.

When Malpighi declared that it could not, their friendship was seriously threatened.

Nonetheless they missed their exchanges of letters, and so the quarrel about the frogs did not last long. Perhaps with the intention of mollifying Malpighi, Borelli wrote him a letter urging him to accept a vacant chair in Messina.

Malpighi never particularly wished to leave Bologna and only left the city when he could no longer endure the ever-constant intrigues and annoyances. He had only been back a year when some people began to recall the old controversies. As a result Borelli's urging led him to decide, and shortly afterwards he started out for Sicily.

He was lucky enough to be invited to stay at the villa of a rich patrician, where he was able to devote himself undisturbed to his interests.

Day by day a new concept, a new idea began to take shape in his mind as his microscope revealed hitherto unknown and unsuspected wonders from the secret world of living organisms.

But he was alone among his colleagues in Messina. The ideas he spoke of were too novel for them. Thus he was forced, as it were, to bombard all of Europe with his letters. He had to find those who were slaves to a similar passion, and the similarity of interests, together with the common Latin language, made possible the exchange of ideas with distant countries without nationalistic bias.

He was accustomed to exchanges with Borelli and other Italian friends. But now the mailcoaches bore letters to Willis in England, to Bartholin in Copenhagen, Swammerdam in Amsterdam, and de la Boe in Antwerp. Thus Malpighi's name came to be known throughout Europe.

Nothing escaped his attention. A goose leg served at the table became an experimental subject on his plate, as did the broken branch of a chestnut tree seen during a walk in the garden. He immediately brought these into his room and put them under the microscope.

About the liver of animals, he came to the conclusion that it makes the bile and not the blood, as was believed. He noticed small protruberances on the arteries inside the kidneys, but at that point he had no idea of their function. "They hang on the blood-vessels," he noted, "like apples on a tree."

Another time he examined the jellified transparent skin of an umbilical cord and the vessels running down it in spiral fashion. But considerably smaller vessels were also visible. And as he strained his eyes to look, the red stream of the blood began to separate into sections. They looked like rolls of coins scattered here and there but without the individual coins separating. He thought these were fat particles (1665).

Malpighi now wanted to summarize his findings in the form of a book. He wanted to surprise the world and take stock of his results. But Borelli dissuaded him, as did his landlord. Both argued that it would be a pity to interrupt his experiments for the sake of the laborious and time-consuming work of writing.

Malpighi admitted that they were right.

He continued his work, but one day news was brought to him concerning a former student. It appeared that he was openly abusing Malpighi, claiming Malpighi was a doctor by inclination rather than by virtue of knowledge, and repeating every-

where that a disease could not be cured any better for knowing the construction of the organs. Therefore it was more important to study the drugs of the ancient Greeks and Arabs
than to spend one's time bending over a microscope. And, no
sooner did Malpighi receive the news of his former student's
attack than he heard of another one — a book, which by its
very title gave an indication of its contents: "Triumph of the
Galenians."

Malpighi lost patience. He collected a whole bookletful of
Galen's errors, enumerating them point by point and showing
how he had since rectified them with the aid of the instruments
of modern science and exact observation. Borelli encouraged
Malpighi to go ahead and have it published.

In the end, however, his "Defense of the Moderns" remained
in his desk.

From time to time he had attacks from kidney stones, but as
soon as his suffering was over for the moment, he returned to
the task of organizing his notes on the construction of internal
organs.

The views and deductions of the ancients appeared almost
comical next to the new knowledge obtained as a result of
experimentation. On the other hand, everything awaiting the
reader in Malpighi's work seemed intricate and incredible, like
the product of someone's unbridled imagination. No one had
ever written such a book before.

It should, of course, be printed in Bologna.

The Council of Messina would have liked to make a contract with him for a further four years but, for the time being,
at his insistence they allowed him to go home to supervise the
printing of his book.

He still had every intention of returning to Messina in the
spring, but once home, his friends, familiar streets, the dry
cool air, took hold of him once more and he thought with
dread of the coming broiling heat of the Sicilian summers.

He decided to remain in Bologna.

The book was published (1666) and life went on without
change, with interesting daily discoveries relieving the apparent monotony of an otherwise uneventful life.

Then one day the mail brought a letter, signed by a stranger: The Secretary of the Royal Society in London called upon him to enter into correspondence, for the members of the Society were greatly interested in his discoveries, and his observations would be read to them.

He was then forty years old and it appeared that scholars were competing with each other to hear his views. This proof of recognition meant far more to him than any temporary victory of words he could have made against his critics.

The Royal Society was interested in crystals, plants, insects, anything which could possibly interest men of science, but most particularly in silkworms. It is very possible that the pounds sterling of certain merchants may have played their part in the secretary's interest in this field.

Malpighi embarked on this task with reluctance. "This was a very tiresome and lengthy assignment, and it wearied me," he wrote later in his autobiography.

After a while, however, his own curiosity was aroused. He was scarcely out of bed after a bout of fever before he sat down to his microscope again, observing the development of the silkworm larvae.

He also spent hours investigating the small heart throbbing in insects' abdomens, which had already aroused Harvey's attention.

After observing glow worms, on his evening walks, he sought to find out what it was that lighted them up. He would hold the bare abdomen under the lens, then dip it in water to see if the light would be extinguished like that of a candle when the wick came into contact with water. But it went on shining. There had to be something containing sulphur for it to remain so under water, Malpighi argued to himself.

By now "it had become such an intellectual enjoyment to see so many and such spectacular wonders of nature in the course of my work that I am unable to describe it with my pen."

Yet before long he was once more made to feel the old hostilities in Bologna.

During one of his lecture, for example, in the very midst of a demonstration, a member of the audience sprang up and began to shout. Every one looked to see who it was.

They knew him: It was one of Malpighi's enemies.

He began berating Malpighi in the roughest language: Only

a complete half-wit would dissect according to Malpighi's instructions, he said. The things he taught were quite impossible. The audience would do' best to leave the lecture room at once. In his beloved home city, Malpighi was bound to think that he might have been better advised to remain in Messina.

Wherever he went he longed to be home, he could not endure to be away from Bologna, but when he was at home, they gave him no peace. In addition, Malpighi was aware that Girolamo Sbaragli, a son of the Malpighi family rivals in Cav-

56. *Marcello Malpighi. (By C. Cignani in the collection of Professor V. Putti, courtesy of Professor L. Munster)*

57. *Girolamo Sbaraglia on a silver coin of the University of Bologna. (Courtesy of Ciba Z. Basel, 1941, from the article of G. DeFrancesco)*

alcore, had since become something of a personage despite his mere thirty years. He was the leader of the Galen worshippers and his slogan, like that of a good peasant who gives thoughtful care to his fruit trees, was: "Cut off what is useless."

               ❅ ❅ ❅

Malpighi concentrated all his efforts on his research. He was now engaged in the study of the life of plants. They could not live without air, just like animals. Did not plants also have some kind of a circulatory mechanism as animals had? Did not water and air course through them in a similar manner as in tubes equipped with valves? He was unable to find valves and à moving center similar to the heart for the time being, but he set his mind to discovering them.

While Malpighi spent long hours beside his microscope to unveil the secrets of the moisture circulation in plants, there were still those who regarded Harvey's discovery of blood circulation in animals as the fantastic imaginings of the sensationalist. Books — two, three hundred — even a thousand years old — kept appearing in new editions and the arguments between supporters of the old order and the adherents of the new theories were by no means settled.

The student in Paris studying the Hippocratic teachings and the wonderful virtues of Avicenna's syrups must often have been in a quandary as to what he really should believe. However, he might come around to more definite views if, despite his parents' and professors' disapproval, he went off to see the evening performance at the Palais Royal where Molière's "Le Malade Imaginaire" was performed.

For many years the famous playwright and actor had been in ill health. He spent great sums of money on physicians, with little result. Thus in "Le Malade Imaginaire" he caricatured the dignified medical profession in the person of the pompous Doctor Defois who on one occasion introduces his somewhat dim-witted son to an assembled company in these words: "His imagination was never lively, nor has he that sparkling wit observed in many . . . . He was ever slow. His tutors had the devil's time to teach him reading and he was nine before he learned . . . . At college he was hard put, but he doggedly stood firm . . . . But I can say without boasting, there is not a candidate for the Bachelor of Physics degree who has entered more noisily into the school disputes. . . . But what pleases me most in Thomas is that he follows my example in blindly following the dictates of the ancients. He will not comprehend nor recognize modern teachings and discoveries."

Thereupon the boy brings out a dissertation written on an enormous scroll, and handing it over to his betrothed, says: "Here is a thesis, in which I lengthily refute that wild new theory concerning the circulation of the blood. With your permission, sir, I herewith tender these first fruits of my genius to the young lady as a token of the esteem in which I hold her."

The medical students, with gallery tickets in their pockets, roared with laughter. Here was one in the eye for the professors. What would the authorities of the Paris University like Jean Riolan or Guy Patin have said?

The play was a success, but a week after the opening performance Molière was taken ill in the middle of the play. With difficulty he pulled through, but in the last scene a convulsion of coughs overwhelmed him, which he tried to make sound as if it would have been laughter. Some in the audience noticed, some others thought it was a masterpiece of acting. The cast of the comedy, however, knew better.

After the end of the performance, still dressed for the part of the dying man, surrounded by actors with their clowns' make-up still on their faces, Molière uttered: "I have a murderous chill." One of the bystanders touched his hand and felt that it was ice cold. They carried him home to his apartment which was not far from the theatre. His wife and a friend rushed away to get a priest — without success. When they arrived back, after half an hour of unrewarded searching, they found Moliére dead, strangled by the blood pouring out of a ruptured vessel in his lung.*

* * *

While the problem of circulation had reached even the stage, Malpighi was trying to understand the development of the heart's formation.

He slid an egg in the process of development into lukewarm water in order to be able to study it, not for a minute, as Aristotle had done, but for hours at least. He noted that the throbbing point in the center of the embryo did not turn into a heart without transition, but first grew lengthwise, became a narrow tube which then began to curve until it ended in an intricate confusion, finally assuming the shape of the heart, hardly perceptibly, with all its ventricles, valves and blood vessels developed from a single straight tube.

But what of the beginning?

The throbbing small tube was red because it contained blood. Did this mean then that the blood and heart came into being simultaneously? Or the blood first, since the heart could only transmit blood? But if blood was made first, where did it circulate meanwhile and what moved it in the absence of a heart?

After much deliberation he put the question aside, erasing it from his list of problems to be solved. It seemed so futile to keep on working at something which could not be explained!

He returned to plants once more.

Letters came from and went to distant countries. There were even some which may have startled him a little.

---

*Those interested in more details on Molière's life and his relationship to the medical profession are advised to read the biographies by B. Matthews and Ramon Fernandez (see BIBLIOGRAPHY).

All those members of the Royal Society who worked in science sent him accounts of their findings. Nationality did not enter into it, rank meant nothing. The only requirement was that the letters should deal with serious scientific subjects. Thus Leeuwenhoek, a simple master optician, could expect the same attention as any university professor. And Malpighi found himself bound to admit that the optician had found out that the small globules in the blood vessels, which he had taken for particles of fat, were not spheres, but disks, and were specially compounded to give the blood its red color.

But this small oversight could not injure his prestige. What he saw and thought was considered so important that scientists arriving from distant countries turned to him for advice; and in 1680 the Royal Society asked him for a portrait.

Despite these unique forms of recognition the opposition in Bologna would not rest. Malpighi decided not to expose himself to any further trouble, and retired. He bought a charming villa, the former residence of the famous Grimaldi family. The small palace belonged to the descendants of Genoa's former rulers and its handsome exterior showed plainly that it had been the home of no ordinary mortal, nor could the man who now moved into it be one.

Malpighi looked forward to a pleasant retirement and a complete absorption in studies, without the nuisance of carrying the burdens of a professor.

It was precisely his wide range of knowledge, based on individual experiment in every field, which galled his antagonists, whom he took pains to avoid. It was impossible for them not to notice the great respect in which he was held in the most distant corners of the world, not to mention the number of his personal friends in Bologna. Perhaps they felt that the homage was given not so much to the man as to the trend, the new way of thought, which was diametrically opposed to their own and which if it were victorious, would demolish them completely.

Sbaragli, who was the chief mover of the opposition camp, finally published a booklet at the end of 1687 in Göttingen, entitled: "Study of Contemporary Physicians."

He listed once again the old objections. Microscopic research in no way furthered the struggle against disease, he wrote. For example, why was it important to know that the blood circulated around such or such globules in the lungs? Everyone knew that animals breathed. Yet who was to say why they breathed? With this new seventeenth-century knowledge it was possible to explain the construction of the lungs, but as to combatting pneumonia, they were no better at it than the ancients.

Then there was the pancreas. Formerly it was thought to be a cushion upon which the stomach rested. Now they had to learn that it is a gland which has an exit tube. But was this important? Did this enable us to cure stomach ailments?

And then the incubated eggs . . . .

At that time such reasoning seemed logical and gave the impression that Malpighi's decades of effort were but the hair-splittings of an amateur scientist, the findings of a grouchy pedant, without any practical use whatsoever.

If Malpighi were to have left the attack unanswered, as he had done several years previously, it would have seemed to many that he was unable to defend himself against such convincing arguments.

He therefore made his reply in a long letter: "You condemn my work, mock it in your writings, so now I shall defend it. But first let us see wherein lies the strength and greatness of everything in which you believe. You claim that diseases are brought about by harmful fluids. Where are these harmful fluids? In the organs and the blood, you say. I for my part have never seen them in the blood, for when a blood vessel is cut open, the blood always appears approximately the same. The "atrabiliary" blood is black, you say, but, you see, it is sufficient to take foaming bright red blood under water for it to turn black also. Or is the "melancholic" blood made by such simple means? I now add a substance to such black blood which should make it even more atrabilic, ordinary salt; and the blood, dark until now, becomes red. What is more, it is sufficient to put the melancholic and dark blood in contact with air and shake it a little for it to regain its former red color. In view of this, what importance can you attach to the changes in the color of the blood, upon which your theory of harmful fluids is based?"

His tone was decided, the examples with which he exposed his opponents' methods of thought were clear and convincing. There could be no doubt that Sbaragli had had the worst of the argument.

But Sbaragli's aim was to make life impossible for Malpighi. The scientific argument, the differences of opinion and disputes about academic questions were merely the means of expressing the primitive hatred of vendetta. The centuries-old feuding between the Malpighis and Sbaraglis had taken this seemingly rational and intellectual turn, for this was in conformity with their communal positions. Had they remained on their farms perhaps Sbaragli would have been more honest and attacked Malpighi with a club.

The memory of a fight between members of the two families some years previously in which Malpighi's younger brother had killed a Sbaragli would not let him rest. He had to have his revenge for Malpighi's successes and affluence — for the Sbaragli blood spilled by a Malpighi — for the great prestige Malpighi enjoyed in Bologna.

One beautiful night in June, 1689, Malpighi was studying kidney tissue through his microscope. At this hour all was quiet and he could finally take advantage of all preliminary study to make advanced observations.

Suddenly he raised his head. Footsteps could be heard from the garden. There was the swaying light of lanterns. He looked out and saw masked figures approaching.

He sprang up, but by then they were inside the room. They overturned furniture, mocked him, sang derisive songs and pranced around him.

He scarcely had time to collect himself, was still smarting under the humiliation of the attack when shortly afterwards a greater blow fell: his house caught fire. He was never able to learn whether it was the result of a fire in the chimney, or the work of arsonists.

The books, notes, plants and insect collections, and the crystal slides which were so important to him with their microscopic data nearly all were consumed by the fire.

Amongst objects hastily rescued only one microscope remained intact and some money he had saved up.

It was a trifle next to all he had owned, but sufficient to kindle the spark necessary to try once more. He would be able to continue, who knew when, but one day he would continue his interrupted work.

Throngs of people came and went, carrying water, clearing up, carting rubble.

A few days later his last remaining microscope and the little money he had left also disappeared in all the upheaval.

* * *

It is almost impossible to believe that Malpighi should not have received a microscope as a gift from one of his friends, and the Royal Society almost certainly would gladly have given him their support. But there are emotional states, a daze induced by a mixture of exhaustion and weariness with life, in which one cannot and does not want to avail oneself of help but would prefer to die.

"I live," Malpighi wrote, "if you can call such inactivity living . . . . I have no other aim but that of distracting my thoughts away from my loss." And even this acceptance was really acquiescence rather than recovery from suffering: "I must accept it as the word of Haeven . . . there is nothing left for me but to study the work of others and enjoy it."

For four years he wrote not a single line. He withdrew within himself and felt nothing but that he was old and ill. At times he was bothered by feelings of nausea, then by pains in the joints, and finally he was attacked by the fever which had been recurring for decades. His friends saw that he was resigning himself to his fate and would die very shortly.

The election of the new pope came at the right moment. He had been Bolognese ambassador under the name of Cardinal Pignatelli, knew Malpighi well and liked him very much. He immediately sent word to him suggesting he move to Rome as first physician to the papal court.

Malpighi did not accept. He gave his illness as his reason, the long journey, his house which he did not want to leave, everything he could think of. If only he did not have to move. He had apparently accepted the thought that he would die.

But Pope Innocent was not the man to be deterred from his plans by a single refusal. He embarked on involved diplomatic tactics, drawing some of Malphigi's beloved students into the argument, and perhaps even the faithful Francesca who had stood by her husband through so many adversities. After some weeks of frequent exchanges of letters, persuasion, entreaties and arguments, Innocent finally succeeded.

In October, 1691, after two weeks' travel, the spires of Rome came into view and on the road a splendid procession wound its way: the pope, to whom kings and princes paid homage, came to receive his old friend, the scientist, whom all of Europe respected, except his own city of Bologna.

Malpighi was given quarters in the immediate vicinity of the pope's residence, in the Quirinal, where he lived three more years without duties or disturbance.

In 1694 he had a stroke. He recovered in a few weeks, but it served as a warning.

He gave his papers to the Royal Society and entrusted his correspondence and other possessions to his students. He left word that he wished to be dissected after his death, in order that his body might give opportunities for further study once it had ceased to be useful for any other purpose. But they were to do this only 30 hours after his death to make sure he was really dead.

Everything happened as he decreed. Two of his best students dissected him. They found the kidney stones which had tormented him so much. When they reached the brain they found one chamber full of blood. They spooned out the dark substance whose circulation had kept him going through sixty-five good and bad years, as long as it had stayed within the intricate network which he had so devotedly studied.

As soon as the blood had broken the rules necessary for the maintenance of life and stepped off its allotted course, it had destroyed him.

Blood vessels were thus destined to be the cause of both Malpighi's death and immortality.

* * *

A few decades later, in the early 1700's, a company of traveling players arrived in a small Italian town. The citizenry discussed the posters on the walls of the houses, gesturing wildly. One of them, who had the reputation of being a literary man, contrived not only to be admitted to rehearsals, but even allowed on the stage.

As he wandered around behind the scenes, his eye was caught by something on the side of one of the wings.

There was a crack in it which someone had tried to repair by pasting sheets of paper over it. These were covered with close writing in dense straight lines. They were scarcely discernible. When he looked up in the gloomy light he observed similar sheets of paper stuck on other parts of the wings, some much the worse for wear, with the text almost obliterated. But as he was always hoping to come upon some rarity, he asked the stage director whose papers these were.

The director had no idea at all, but said he had more like them, which he had not yet used for pasting up the holes and which he had bought very cheap, instead of expensive packing paper or newspaper.

The literary man asked for a few pages and took them to his lodgings. He tried to read them, but did not understand what they said. They mentioned "globules", "fibers," and "blood vessels," and the text was illustrated with incomprehensible diagrams. He was a little annoyed by the whole thing, but took the sheets along to his doctor friends to see if they might be interested.

He turned out to have made a shrewd guess. They were Malpighi's manuscripts.

Malpighi's discoveries however would not have been lost even if the bibliophile had not been interested in the walls of the theatre, for Malpighi and his work would have lived on the strength of his well known letters and already published books.

❉   ❉   ❉

With Malpighi's discovery of the capillary blood vessels the last uncertainty in the theory of blood circulation was abolished. It was proved that the path is one-way, continuous and uninterrupted, whether part of it leads from the heart through the pulmonary arteries and lung to the left auricle, or along a greater circle from the heart through the aorta to all tissues of the body, where the blood collects in the veins and comes back again to the heart.

The way to the discovery of the blood circulation was a long and difficult one. Some of the steps forward were the result of a chance glimpse and a happy coincidence; but most of them were the fruits of a lifetime's steady concentration.

These often long voyages of discovery were undertaken by men of unusual character. They all had imagination and a penetrating ability to observe things in their undisguised simplicity. Most of these men were vain and self-confident to a degree which was almost revolting; such characteristics, however, supplied them with power and endurance to pursue their obsessive curiosity.

The strange thing about them was that they differed so much from each other. The scope of their talent, their character, origins, habits, religion, nationality, even the age at which they were creative, differed. It is notable that the individual talents of several of the discoverers were by no means exceptional. Other people have been bestowed with similar, or sometimes greater natural gifts, yet they were not as creative as our discoverers were.

The discoverers of blood circulation had no fancy technical equipment to help them, except for Malpighi with his microscope. But it has to be mentioned that more than a thousand years before, mankind already knew about the magnifying power of lenses; and the shortsighted Emperor Nero used to look at his victims through one of them in the Roman arena. A magnifying glass was incorporated into the autopsy inventory of Leonardo da Vinci, but more than a hundred years had to pass before medical people started to use it more extensively for research. Yet the discovery of pulmonary circulation came from hard and constant looking, *without instruments,* at the insides of dead and live bodies. Veins and arteries were cut, then the different color shades of blood pouring out of them were carefully watched. Harvey's crucial experiment to prove the complete circle of blood circulation by tying the great veins or the aorta of the fish did not require, technically, more than a string!

It appears that the interest in raising questions at all and then the ability to reliably prove or disprove any offered answers are the basic factors determining progress. In the course of history such an approach to physical phenomena has appeared in periods in which most other intellectual activities have been stimulated, too. This is why the discoveries concerning the flow of blood were propelled in times when astronomy, technology, and the detection of physical laws were also advancing. Even in the domain of literature, philosophy and arts, progress as well as stagnation came in the same centuries. Different fields affect one another. In ancient Greece the invention of the water-clock triggered some explanations of the pulse. In the 16th century the concept of the circulation of blood was very likely affected by the discovery of the "circular" movements of the "heavenly bodies" talked about extensively in those days. But beyond the immediate influence in various disciplines, the way *how* to get an answer on a set question seems to be the clue to explain progress. The method which insisted on checking a concept before taking it for granted, no matter how reasonable it appeared; which insisted on setting examples to reduplicate nature for easier checking; in other words, the experimental method, was what pushed science, medicine and technology forward.

People did not apply this method often in ancient days. It is a lengthy way to reach certainty, and after much work it might finally prove that one was not right in his initial opinion. But no matter how uncomfortable it was, and is, to be undecided about something for a long time, or to give up familiar explanations about phenomena, some people rather accepted these inconveniences in olden times, too, as they preferred the cumbersome search for truth to the easy swallowing of unproved opinions. We have learned a lot from such people, not only in facts, but in the ways to acquire new knowledge. In spite of this, if we are frank enough with ourselves, we have to admit that even in our advanced present age we do not always follow their example in really proving opinions before giving credence to them. And we must not think of medicine and natural sciences alone . . .

When one muses over the adventurous lives of the discoverers of blood circulation, one sees that, different as those men were in many respects, in one respect — in their way of trying to get answers from nature — they all were very similar. Whenever they were led to presume something to be true, they paused.

They did not give full credit to their presumption. They did not believe — just because something was made plausible by common usage, scientific or philosophic fashion, tradition, authority or everybody else's conviction. Additionally, they had the rare sense not to believe even in their own cherished visions unless they vigorously checked them first. And, as they did with their own thoughts, so they checked and sifted other people's teachings, written words, well-established beliefs.

This *way of thinking* is the clue to their success — and to progress for all of us.

BIOGRAPHICAL REFERENCES

■

Alaric (c. 370-410), King of the Visigoths. After allying himself with
the Emperor Theodosius, he raided Athens and later, seizing
upon the controversies dividing the leaders of Italy, became
the first "barbarian" to besiege and capture Rome.

Alberti, Leone Battista (1404-1472), all-around typical Renaissance
genius — sculptor, painter, but mainly architect; also a good
sportsman. Spent much of his time in Florence and was idol of
the young artists, among them Leonardo da Vinci.

Albertus Magnus (1206?-1280), German Scholastic philosopher
and Dominican friar.

Alexander VI (1430-1503), Borgia pope and father of Cesare Borgia.
A capable, but immoral ruler. Set up the "line of demarcation"
which divided the newly discovered American territories of
Spain and Portugal and which prevented a major clash between them. This line was respected for several centuries.

Alexander the Great (356-323 B.C.), Macedonian king and the mightiest ruler of ancient times. Conquered the Near East, Egypt,
and part of India, which after his death were divided among
his former generals: Seleucus Nicator, Ptolemy Soter and Ly-

251

simachus. From the Straits of Gibraltar to the Indus River, Alexander created a uniform economic and cultural world with the common language of Greek. Was tutored by Aristotle, whose views must have influenced him to a considerable extent.

Al Nafiis (13th century), Arab physician. His description of the pulmonary (lesser) circulation has only recently received recognition, since previously his works were overshadowed by the more famous Ibn Sina (Avicenna).

Anaxagoras (c.500-430 B.C.), Greek philosopher. Maintained that everything in the material world consisted of a mixture of similar things differing only in the ratios of one to the other. ("A portion of everything is in everything.")

Anghiera, Pietro Martyr d' (1457-1526), Italian historian and physician, who lived in Spain. Had personal contact with the great explorers of his time such as Columbus, Magellan and Vasco de Gama.

Antiochus (325-261 B.C.), later called Soter of Syria. King of most of the Near Eastern countries after the death of his father, Seleucus.

Archimedes (c.287-212 B.C.), Greek mathematician and inventor of several machines. Studied in Alexandria and knew the works of Aristarchus and Eratosthenes well.

Argyropoulos, John (1415-1487), Greek humanist. Fled to Florence from the Turks when they took Byzantinum.

Aristarchus (c.310-230 B.C.), Greek philosopher and astronomer in Alexandria. Taught that the earth moved around the sun; also gave figures for the relative distances of the sun and moon.

Aristotle (c.384-322 B.C.), Greek philosopher, disciple of Plato and tutor of Alexander the Great. His treatises, commonly referred to as the 'Organum', include detailed information on the humanities as well as the natural sciences. His views were regarded as the chief source of knowledge not only in ancient Greek and Roman times, but also in the Christian Middle Ages and quite late in the 16th and 17th centuries. Because Christian philosophers many times accepted his teachings too literally, the evolution of the experimental sciences in the Renaissance was often hindered rather than advanced. His encyclopedia described some of the earliest experiments in medicine.

Asclepiades of Prusa (?-96 B.C.), Greek physician working in the latter part of his life in Rome. Founded a famous school for physicians.

Attila (406-453), King of the Huns. His raids on the Eastern Roman Empire and Northern Italy gained him the title of "Scourge of God."

Augustus, Octavianus (63 B.C.-14 A.D.), nephew of Julius Caesar, and the first Roman emperor. His motto "festina lente" (make haste slowly) made him appear less brilliant than his uncle;

however, it apparently earned him more success. A good organizer and a shrewd observer of economics and the weaknesses of his opponents, he was the man who brought peace and stability to the revolution-ridden city of Rome. He is said to have told his wife before dying: "I hope I made a good performance on my stage."

Aurelianus, Lucius Domitius (c.213-275 A.D.), Roman emperor. Was successful in the repelling of the barbaric tribes behind the Danubian frontiers. Fortified Rome with a mighty wall twelve miles in circumference.

Avicenna: see *Ibn Sina.*

Bacon, Sir Francis, Baron of Verulam (1561-1626), English philosopher and statesman. His practical philosophy had considerable influence on contemporary thinking. Was the first influential politician to call attention to the importance of the natural sciences.

Bacon, Roger (1214-1292), English philosopher. (Called by his contemporaries 'doctor mirabilis'.) His works on natural philosophy were condemned partly because of his quite critical remarks about Saint Thomas and Albertus Magnus. Foresaw many of our present technical achievements.

Baersdorf, Cornelius (c.1550), Dutch court physician of Philip II. Was the senior and chief of the other five or six consultant court physicians (one of whom was Vesalius).

Balboa, Nuñez de (1475-1517), Spanish explorer. Was the first European to see the Pacific in 1513.

Bartholin, Thomas (1616-1680), Danish anatomist. Was one of a well-known family of professors and scholars.

Boccaccio, Giovanni (1313-1375), Italian humanist and poet, whose collection of stories, the 'Decameron', is still read today.

Boniface VIII, Pope (1235-1303). Was one of the few of his era who undertook long journeys, visiting even England when he was a young diplomat of the Vatican.

Borelli, Giovanni Alfonso (1608-1619), Italian physiologist and physicist, and professor at the Universities of Messina and Pisa.

Borgia, Alexander: see *Alexander VI.*

Borgia, Cesare (1476-1507), quick-witted and talented son of Pope Alexander VI. At the time Leonardo da Vinci was in his service, was the general of the papal army. Machiavelli used him as an example of a shrewd ruler in his book 'The Prince'.

Botticelli, Sandro (1444-1510), Florentine painter. First studied in the workshop of the Pollaiuolo brothers and later went to Verrocchio where he became the colleague of Perugino and Leonardo da Vinci. Afterwards came under the influence of Savonarola. The paintings of his final period are purely religious and symbolic in character.

Brunelleschi, Filippo (1377-1446), first great Renaissance architect (also sculptor).

Brutus, Marcus Junius (78-42 B.C.). Was the leader of the conspiracy against Julius Caesar, in spite of Caesar's magnanimous and friendly behavior towards him. Committed suicide after being defeated by Marc Anthony and Octavian.

Bucer, Martin (1491-1551), German Protestant reformer.

Buckingham, George Villiers (1592-1628), English statesman with the talents of a courtier, and a favorite of King Charles I.

Caesar, Gaius Julius (102?-44 B.C.), the greatest Roman military leader, statesman and author. Was the founder and organizer of the large scale Roman Empire which we usually talk about. Clear and determined in his aims, sometimes without scruples in order to achieve might, he was by no means oppressive. None of the subsequent leaders of Rome could have matched his talents, and very few his democratic way of thinking.

Calcar, Jan Stephen (1499-1545). Dutch painter, pupil of Titian, and friend of Vesalius, for whose 'Anatomy' Calcar drew the illustrations.

Calvin, John (1509-1564), French Protestant reformer. In 1533 had to flee Paris because of his reforming opinions. He finally settled in Geneva, Switzerland. The austerity he wanted people to adapt was deeply resented, and he was forced to leave the city. After a short time, was recalled, and due to his virtues and great knowledge was regarded as the spiritual leader of Geneva. However, the opposition for a long time tried to oust him, and because there was no overt possibility of doing this, they grasped every possible opportunity to undermine Calvin's might. There is a strong possibility that during the trial of Servetus, the latter was secretly incited to resist Calvin by some of the leaders of this opposition.

Carpi, Berengario (?-1530), Italian anatomist at the University of Bologna.

Castellion, Sebastian (1515-1563), French humanist and literary foe of Calvin. Lived in Basel at the time Vesalius was visiting his publisher there, preparing the second edition of his book. Whether Vesalius and Castellion knew each other, we can not be certain.

Cato, Marcus Portius (95-46 B.C.), author and statesman, one of the leaders of the Roman Senate and an ardent opponent of Caesar.

Celsus, Aurelius Cornelius (42 B.C.-37 A.D.), Roman patrician and writer of the only Roman medical textbook.

Cesalpino, Andrea (1519-1603), Italian philosopher, botanist and physician. Professor of medicine in Pisa and later court physician to Pope Clement VIII. He, himself, was called by his contemporaries 'the pope of philosophers'.

Charles I (1600-1649), King of Great Britain and Ireland. Was the supporter and friend of William Harvey. Of good intention, but obstinate and not very lucky in choosing the best possible solution in difficult circumstances, his life was a chain of unsuccessful events ending with his execution during the English Revolution.

Charles V (1500-1558), 'Roman Emperor', born a Hapsburg. His constant effort throughout his reign was to mold a united Europe. However, his aims could not be fulfilled in an era of exceptionally overwhelming internal and external difficulties.

Charles VIII (1470-1498), King of France. Claimed the kingdom of Naples and was aided in his campaign (1494) by Lodovico Sforza. His French army is said to have first spread syphilis (hence the contemporary name 'French disease').

Christina (1626-1689), Queen of Sweden. Patroness of artists and scientists (Descartes and Borelli among them).

Cleopatra (69-30 B.C.), Queen of Egypt and member of the Ptolemaic dynasty. Was the mistress of Caesar and bore him a son, Caesarion, who was put to death by Octavian, later Emperor Augustus.

Columbus, Realdo (Colombo) (1510?-1559), Italian anatomist. In Padua was the pupil and later successor of Vesalius. Is famous for the discovery of the pulmonary (lesser) circulation and also for the detailed description of the ear ossicles and some cranial nerves.

Columbus, Christopher (Christoforo Colombo) (1446-1506), Italian explorer. Studied astonomy and geometry at the University of Pavia where Leonardo da Vinci visited so many times ten to fifteen years later.

Commodus (Lucius Aelius Aurelianus) (161-192), Roman emperor and son of Marcus Aurelius, one of the worst tyrants.

Copernicus (Nicolas Kopernik) (1473-1543), Polish astronomer. Studied medicine from 1501 to 1505 in Padua. His epoch-making treatise on the heliocentric system was published in 1543, the same year that Vesalius' book was printed.

Cromwell, Oliver (1599-1658), Lord Protector of England and a leading figure of the English Revolution.

Demetrius (4th century), Greek philosopher, with Ptolemy Soter, the co-founder of the Alexandrian library and museum.

Democritus (465?-400? B.C.), Greek philosopher. The first promoter of an atomic theory which is astonishingly modern in some details.

Descartes, René (1596-1650), French philosopher. Was the first well-known man to support Harvey's new concept of the blood circulation.

Dolet, Étienne (1509-1546), French scholar and printer in Lyon. Was burned at the stake in Paris.

Donatello (1386-1466), Italian sculptor and architect, living in Florence.

Dürer, Albrecht (1471-1528), German painter and engraver, of Hungarian extraction. Visited Italy and was greatly impressed by Titian.

Elizabeth (1533-1603), Queen of England and Ireland, and child of Henry VIII.

Ent, Sir George (17th century), English physician and Harvey's young contemporary.

Erasistratus (310-c. 240 B.C.), most famous Alexandrinian physician and first ardent representative of organ pathology. Was the first to describe the valves in the heart and give them their names.

Eratosthenes (276-194 B.C.), Greek astonomer in Alexandria.

Euclid (3rd century B.C.), Greek mathematician who taught in Alexandria during the reigns of the first two Ptolemies.

Fabricius (Fabrizio d'Acquapendente) (1537-1619), Italian anatomist and surgeon. Was one of the first to describe the valves in the veins. Was also William Harvey's tutor in Padua.

Fallopia, Gabriele (1523-1562), Paduan anatomist.

Farel, Guillame (1489-1565), French reformer and Calvin's best friend. During the trial of Servetus, was present in court all the time, instead of Calvin, until the sentence had been passed.

Ferdinand I (1503-1564), 'Roman Emperor', younger brother and later successor of Charles V.

Ficino, Marsilio (1433-1499), Italian philosopher. Was one of the leading personages in the Florentine 'Platonic Academy' founded by Cosimo de Medici.

Francis I (1494-1547), King of France. In his young years spent most of his time in entertainments (he was the model of the 'Prince' in the opera 'Rigoletto'). In later years, was involved in a life-long struggle against Emperor Charles V, which occasionally forced him into indulgence towards the Protestants. His sister, Marguerite de Navarre, helped the Protestants as much as she could. Francis was the patron of several excellent artists. Was a typical Renaissance ruler with all the virtues and vices characteristic thereof.

Frederick II (1194-1250), 'Holy Roman Emperor'.

Fugger, the name of a German family of merchants. They acquired a tremendous fortune which made them as powerful as their Italian counterparts, the Medicis.

Galen (Claudius Galenus) (138-201 A.D.), last great Greek physician of Alexandrinian influence. His works were standard medical references for 1500 years, outliving the Roman and Arab empires. His authority finally began to be shattered by the revolutionary change in values of the Renaissance and the Reformation.

Galilei, Galileo (1564-1642), Italian astronomer and native of Florence. In the years of Harvey's Paduan residence, was a young, self-confident, exuberant professor at the University. At the same time corresponded with Kepler, the German astronomer, about the Copernican solar system. Certainly in those times, the circular movement (circulatio) of the planets was the fashionable conversation piece among scientific people. Galileo was the good friend of Fabrizio and Paolo Sarpi, people who must have talked in Harvey's presence about the circular movements of the,planets as well as the flowing of the blood.

Ghiberti, Lorenzo(1378-1455), Florentine painter.

Ghirlandaio, Domenico (1449-1494), Florentine painter.

Giotto, Bondone (1276-1337), Florentine painter and sculptor.

Günther von Andernach (1487-1574), German anatomist, lecturing in Paris in Vesalius' and Servetus' time. Was also the court physician of Francis I, the French king, but later was obliged to flee Paris because of his Protestant beliefs.

Hadrian (Publius, Aelius Hadrianus) (76-138), Roman emperor.

Hannibal (247-183 B.C.), Carthaginian general who crossed the Alps to invade Italy.

Harun al-Raschid (764-809), caliph of Baghdad. His reign was notable for its patronage of poets, jurists and scholars.

Harvey, William (1578-1657), English physician and the discoverer of the blood circulation. Harvey was the first not only to describe the circulation in full detail, but to prove it experimentally.

Herophilus (3rd century B.C.), Greek physician and grandson of Aristotle. Is said to have been the first to dissect human corpses, with the permission of Ptolemy Philadelphus. Very likely, was some ten to twenty years older than Erasistratus.

Hipparchus (190-125 B.C.), Greek astronomer in Alexandria.

Hippocrates (460?-355 B.C.), Greek physician, and the first great figure of medical history. His medical encyclopedia 'Corpus Hippocraticum', written presumably with many contributors, contains a mass of good observation and sound reasoning. Liked to explain disease as an improper relationship of the 'four cardinal fluids' (a precursor of the modern concept of electrolyte balance and hormonal disturbances?).

Hofmann, Caspar (1572-1648), German professor of anatomy. Harvey visited him while he was on his journey to Vienna. Hofmann did not give credit to Harvey's new theory; however, there is evidence that the two corresponded later, and this might account for Hofmann's more lenient opinion about the circulation in later years.

Homer, (9th century B.C.), ancient Greek poet.

Huss, John (1369-1415), Bohemian religious reformer and martyr.

Ibn Sina (Avicenna) (980-1037), Persian philosopher and physician.

His 'Canon' was regarded until the late Renaissance as one of the best reference works in medicine. Leonardo da Vinci refers to his views several times.

Innocent XI (1611-1689), Pope. The patron of Malpighi. Was instrumental in driving the Turks out of Austria and Hungary (the 'Holy Alliance').

James I (1566-1625), King of England and son of Mary, Queen of Scots. Was a well-intentioned ruler, but was induced to try and solve religious problems which probably nobody could have solved in the heated atmosphere of that age.

Jansen, H. (?-1619), Dutch spectacle maker and his son Zacharias were the inventors of the telescope and microscope.

Jonson, Ben (1573-1637), English dramatist and poet, and good friend of Shakespeare.

Laguna, Andreas (1499-1560), Spanish court physician of Emperor Charles V. As such, must have known Vesalius very well.

Leeuwenhoek, Anthony van (1632-1723), self-taught Dutch naturalist, who contributed essential observations to microscopic anatomy. Was the first to recognize the specific role of the red blood cells, which were seen but explained in a different manner (and wrongly) by Malpighi.

Leo X (Giovanni de Medici) (1475-1521), Pope. Favored learning, literature and art, and supported Raphael, Michelangelo and others. During his pontificate, Luther launched the Reformation.

Leonardo da Vinci (1452-1519), Italian painter, sculptor, architect and scientist. One can hardly point to an artistic or scientific problem which he did not tackle.

Lippershey, H. (beginning of the 17th century) Dutch spectacle maker, the inventor with the two Janssens of the telescope and microscope.

Louis XII (1462-1515), French king.

Loyola, Ignatius (1491-1556), Spanish noble and career officer, who after having become lame in battle, became a priest and later founded the Jesuit order.

Luther, Martin (1483-1546), German reformer. Visited Rome at about the time when Leonardo da Vinci was resident there in Pope Leo X's court. Luther's action in 1519 against the papal domination of the Christian religion actually started the Reformation.

Lysimachus (361-281 B.C.), Macedonian general of Alexander the Great.

Machiavelli, Niccolo (1469-1527), Italian statesman, historian and writer. Was the Florentinian ambassador to Cesare Borgia when Leonardo da Vinci was Cesare's military engineer. Machiavelli took Cesare as an example of a shrewd, ruthless but politically successful leader in his book 'The Prince', deplored by many, but followed by more.

Magellan, Ferdinand (1480-1521), Portuguese navigator. Was to find the Strait to the Pacific in South America which is called by his name; and was the first European to see the Philippine Islands.

Maimonides (Moses Ben Maimon) (1135-1204), Jewish philosopher, talmudist and physician. After being forced to flee Cordoba, settled in Cairo, where he became the recognized head of the Jewish community of Egypt.

Malpighi, Marcello (1628-1694), Italian anatomist and founder of microscopic anatomy.

Marco Polo (1254-1324), Italian traveler, who wrote an enjoyable report on his travels (as a Venetian tradesman) in the Far East and in the Great Moguls' Mongol empire.

Marcus Aurelius, Antoninus (121-180), Roman emperor. Was a fine statesman and a respected stoic philosopher.

Marguerite de Navarre (1497-1549), queen of a small kingdom, and sister of the French king, Francis I. In addition to her beauty, was also the author of several poetic works. She favored the Protestants at a time and place when this involved a certain risk.

Martialis, Marcus Valerius (40-103 A.D.), Roman poet known for his witty and sarcastic epigrams.

Massari, Bartolommeo (17th century), Italian professor of anatomy at Bologna, and teacher and father-in-law of Malpighi. Founded an unconventional 'Coro anatomico' — a society to enhance studies in anatomy.

Matthias, Corvinus (1440-1490), Hungarian king, humanist, general and statesman. The mightiest Renaissance king in Central Europe. Some rescued volumes of his library are still admired ("Corvina's"). The rest of his collections (the 300 statues and many paintings including the works of Leonardo and his master Verrocchio) were destroyed by the Ottoman Turks.

Maximinius Thrax (Gaius Julius) (173-238), the first Roman emperor of 'barbarian' origin.

Medici, Cosimo (1389-1464), 'the elder', honored for his many contributions in Florence as 'pater patriae'.

Medici, Cosimo (1520-1574), grand duke of Tuscany, and ruthless ruler of his small state. He executed some lasting public works and supported the Universities of Pisa and Siena.

Medici, Giovanni: see *Leo X.*

Medici, Giuliano (?-1516), younger brother of Pope Leo X. Was Leonardo da Vinci's patron for a short time, otherwise he was an unremarkable person.

Medici, Lorenzo de ('The Magnificent') (1449-1492), a grandson of Cosimo the elder. A highly cultured leader of Florence and a supporter of artists.

Melanchthon, Philippe (1497-1560), a leading personage of the Reformation. Was a calm, well-educated personality and a friend of Calvin.

Methrodorus (4th century B.C.), Greek physician, son-in-law of Aristotle, and teacher of Erasistratus.

Michelangelo, Buonarotti (1475-1564), Florentine painter and sculptor, 23 years younger than Leonardo da Vinci.

Molière (Jean Baptiste Poquelin) (1622-1673), French writer of comedies, and favored by Louis XIV.

Mondino de Luzzi (1270-1326), Italian anatomist in Bologna.

Octavianus: see *Augustus.*

Oporinus (Herbster, John) (1507-1568), Swiss publisher in Basel, and friend of Vesalius.

Paracelsus (Theophrastus von Hohenheim) (1493-1541), Swiss physician, who contributed in particular to pharmacology.

Patin, Guy (1602-1672), French anatomist. At first was a publisher, but later acquired lasting fame by writing 'letters' which involved political personages and which became well known because of the typical French 'piquanterie' involved in them.

Perugino, Pietro (1450-1524), Italian painter who studied in Verrocchio's studio with Botticelli and Leonardo da Vinci.

Petrarch (Francesco Petrarca) (1304-1374), poet and humanist, and descendant of a Florentine family. Together with Dante and Boccaccio, is one of the greatest figures in Italian literature.

Philip II (1527-1598), King of Spain and son of Emperor Charles V.

Pliny (Gaius Plinius Secundus) (c.23-79 A.D.), Roman author of books on divergent topics. His 'Natural History in Thirty-Seven Books' is the first ancient scientific encyclopedia.

Pollaiuolo, Antonio, Piero and Simone. All three were painters in Leonardo da Vinci's time. They practiced anatomical dissections as part of their artistic studies.

Pompey (Gaius Pompeius) (106-48 B.C.), Roman statesman and successful general of the Roman army and navy. He was the last hope of the old-fashioned aristocracy opposing the leadership of Caesar.

Praxagoras (4th century B.C.), Greek physician. Pointed out the difference between the arteries and the veins for the first time.

Ptolemy Ceraunus (315?-279 B.C.), brother of Ptolemy Philadelphus, who, after leaving Egypt and having killed Selecus, became king of Macedonia.

Ptolemy, Claudius (c.100-150 A.D.), Alexandrian mathematician, astronomer and geographer. Was not related to the dynasty of the same name.

Ptolemy, Dionysus (61-47 B.C.), younger brother and according to Egyptian custom husband of Cleopatra. Died in the war against Caesar, when he was only seventeen years old.

Ptolemy, Philadelphus (309-246 B.C.), son of Ptolemy Soter. Contributed a great deal to the fame of the Alexandrinian library by his economic support and personal presence at the scientists' meetings.

Ptolemy Soter (367-283 B.C.), one of Alexander the Great's most trusted generals, and later a self-made king and founder of the Ptolemaic dynasty which ruled over Egypt for almost three centuries. An outstanding military writer, a patron of letters, and founder of the Alexandrinian Museum and Library which was unequalled in concept for about fifteen-hundred years thereafter.

Pythagoras (6th century B.C.), Greek philosopher and mathematician and astronomer. One of the first to teach that the earth is spherical.

Rabelais, Francois (c. 1495-1555), French author of 'Pantagruel and Gargantua', satirical scripts which mocked many authorities, especially clerical ones. Being a Franciscan friar, also attended medical school; was the acting physician at the Hotel Dieu hospital in Lyon, lectured on anatomy at the time of Servetus' residence there. Very likely they knew each other.

Raleigh, Sir Walter (1552-1616), British explorer and favorite of Queen Elizabeth. At the beginning of King James' reign, was put into the Tower for thirteen years. After he was released, once again got into trouble with the Spaniards and was sentenced to death at their request.

Raphael, Sanzio (1483-1520), one of the most talented and certainly the most successful painter of the Renaissance.

Reina, Francesco de la (16th century), Spanish veterinarian and contemporary of Servetus.

Rhases (850-923), Persian physician.

Richelieu, Armand Jean (1585-1642), cardinal, French statesman, chief advisor of French kings.

Riolan, Jean the Younger (1577-1657), French professor of anatomy in Paris and court physician of the French kings Henry IV and Louis XIII. As son of a famous anatomist of the same name, attended medical school at the University of Padua and very likely knew Harvey in their student years. Also there is possibility that they met in the mid-1640's, some years prior to their discussion in London when Riolan acted as part of the ambassadorial entourage of the French Queen Maria (de Medici) to the English court.

Sarpi, Paolo (1522-1626), Italian historian and mathematician. Was the friend of Galileo and Fabrizio. Harvey must have seen him more than once in his Paduan years. Sarpi wrote a treatise on the movement of blood which was lost with his other manuscripts in a fire in the eighteenth century. This manuscript is said to have dealt with the blood flow in the veins in relation to the valves of the veins. Sarpi and Fabrizio must have talked about the matter in Harvey's presence.

Sbaraglia, Gian Girolamo (1641-1710), Italian professor of anatomy at Bologna, and the foe of Malpighi.

Seleucus Nicator (356-281 B.C.), one of Alexander the Great's generals. After much struggling, he made himself king of what we know today as the Near East (but not Egypt).

Severus Septimius (146-211 A.D.). After he became Roman emperor, introduced a rather rigid military rule in his administration. Having been in Africa and having spent most of his time outside of Rome, maintained his foreign accent until his death. Was the first Roman emperor to favor foreigners in military posts.

Servetus (Miguel Servede y Reves) (1509-1553), religious reformer and physician. In Paris, was the pupil of Günther von Andernach and Sylvius; was also the colleague of Vesalius and the friend of Symporien Champier, the celebrated French scholar and physician in Lyon. Was probably acquainted with Rabelais, the French satirical author, scholar and physician.

Sforza, Lodovico (1451-1508), Duke of Milan. More shrewd than foresighted, more hesitating than determined, he was driven from his dukedom by the force of circumstances he was unable to meet. In spite of his weaknesses, his rule belongs to the glorious years of Milan's history.

Shakespeare, William (1564-1616). His best-known works were written during the reign of Queen Elizabeth. Ben Jonson and Sir Walter Raleigh were personal friends. Some historians have suggested that the rival mentioned in his sonnets might have been William Harvey, and they even point to some lines in the 'Winter's Tale' claiming to represent knowledge of the blood circulation; but these are all pious misinterpretations in the clear light of facts.

Strafford, Thomas Wentworth (1593-1641), English statesman. One of the important personalities in the English Revolution ("Black Tom").

Swammerdam, John (1637-1680), Dutch pioneer of microscopic anatomy in Amsterdam.

Sylvius, Francois Jacques Dubois (16th century), French anatomist and teacher of Vesalius and Servetus.

Theodosius I, The Great (346-395), Eastern Roman Emperor.

Titian (Titiano Vecellio) (c.1477-1576), Italian Renaissance painter. Painted Emperor Charles V several times, and the French king, Francis I, as well. One of his pupils, Calcar, provided the anatomical illustrations for the books by Vesalius.

Torre, Marcantonio della (1478-1511), Italian anatomist and friend of Leonardo da Vinci.

Urban VIII (1568-1644), Pope. Was the pope who dealt with Galileo in the two historical trials of 1616 and 1633.

Usaibiyaa (13th century), Arab physician. His biographies of Arab physicians were a major contribution and are still recognized as a source of information in the history of medicine.

Valverde, Juan de Hamusco (16th century), Spanish physician and contemporary of Vesalius and Colombo.

Van Dyck, Sir Anthony (1599-1641), Flemish painter. He spent some of his later years in London, painting portraits of the nobility and of King Charles I and his family. Belonging to the Court he must have known Harvey.

Varro, Marcus Terentius (116-27 B.C.). The most learned man of his era and the most voluminous Roman writer (he wrote at least seventy-four separate works).

Verrocchio, Andrea (1435-1488), Florentine painter and sculptor. His studio was the place where Leonardo da Vinci, Botticelli, Lorenzo di Credi, Perugino and many others studied.

Verus, Lucius Aurelius (130-169), Roman emperor.

Vesalius, Andreas (1514-1564), first modern anatomist. Was of Flemish extraction, coming from a family of highly educated and respectable physicians, pharmacists and scholars.

Vespucci, Amerigo (1451-1512), Florentine merchant of high education. His journeys with Columbus were probably undertaken on behalf of the Medicis. His letters give an account of his travels in the 'Indies', which he first recognized as a new continent. His letters were translated and printed in several languages with a large success, and they made him very popular even in the first decade of the fifteen-hundreds. The portrait that Leonardo da Vinci drew of him is lost.

Vitruvius (Marcus Vitruvius Pollio), a contemporary of Augustus and a Roman architect and engineer. His theoretical works were extensively studied by the Renaissance architects who obviously learned much from him.

Waal, Jan de (1604-1649), Dutch anatomist. Was the first to oppose Harvey's views on circulation, but later became convinced of the correctness of Harvey's theory by his own experiments. Described his supporting proofs in a letter to Bartholin.

Xavier, Francisco de (1506-1552), Jesuit missionary, 'Apostle of the Indies'. In 1537, devoted his time to hospital work in Venice during the same year that Vesalius also spent some months in Venetian hospitals.

Zwingli, Huldreich (1484-1531), Swiss Protestant reformer.

BIBLIOGRAPHY

■

GENERAL REFERENCES

BUTTERFIELD, H.M.A.   *The Origins of Modern Science*, New York, Macmillan, 1957.

CASTIGLIONI, A.   *Storia della Medicina*, Verona, Mondadori, 1948.

DAREMBERG, CH.   *Histoire des Sciences Medicales*, Paris, Bailliere, 1870.

DARMSTAEDTER, L. and DU BOIS-RAYMOND, R.   4000 *Jahre Pionier Arbeit*, Berlin, Stargardt, 1904.

FELDHAUS, F. M.   *Lexicon der Erfindungen und Entdeckungen*, Heidelberg, Winter, 1904.

GARRISON, F.H.   *An Introduction to the History of Medicine*, Philadelphia and London, Saunders, 1929.

HAESER, H.   *Geschichte der Medizin*, Jena, Dufft, 1875.

IRSAY, S.   *Histoire des Universités*, Paris, 1933.

LANGER, W.L.   *An Encyclopedia of World History*, Boston, Houghton Mifflin, 1948.

MAJOR, R.H.   *A History of Medicine*, Springfield, Ill., Thomas, 1954.

MASON, S.F.   *Main Currents of Scientific Thought*, New York, Abelard-Schuman, 1956.

265

NEUBURGER, M. and PAGEL, J. *Handbuch der Geschichte der Medizin,* Jena, G. Fischer, 1902.

SIGERIST, H.E. *Man and Medicine,* London, Allen and Unwin, 1932.

SINGER, C.J. *A Short History of Medicine,* Oxford, The Clarendon Press, 1928.

SPECIAL REFERENCES

Chapter I.

ARISTOTLE *Parts of Animals,* Transl. E.S. FOSTER, London-Cambridge, Mass., Harvard University Press, 1911.

BONNET, H. *Reallexicon der aegyptischen Religions-geschichte,* Berlin, Gruyter, 1952.

CROISET, M. *Culture Greque* (Hungarian transl.), Budapest, Atheneum, 1938.

DOBROVITS, A. *Egyptian influence upon ancient Greece* (Hungarian), Budapest, Atheneum, 1908.

ERMAN, A. *Aegypten,* Tubingen, 1885.

GORDON, B.L. *Medicine Throughout Antiquity,* Philadelphia, Davis, 1949.

HINTZSCHE, E. "Uber das anatomische Wissen Galens und seiner Vorlaufer," *Ciba, Z.* No. 96, Basel, 1944.

HOMER *The Odyssey,* New York, Oxford Univ. Press, 1932.

HORANSZKY, J. *The Science of the Greek Enlightenment Period* (Hungarian), Budapest, Academy of Science Press, 1910.

JOACHIM, H. *Papyros Ebers,* Berlin, Reimer, 1890.

KEES, H. *Kulturgeschichte des alten Orients Aegypten* (Handb.d. Altertumswiss.), Munchen, Beck, 1933.

MARTIN, R.A. *Mummies,* Chicago, Cult. Hist. Museum, 1945.

MENDELSOHN, S. *Die Function der Pulsadern und des Kreislaufes in der altrabbinischen Literatur,* Jena, Fischer, 1926.

MUEHSAM, E. "Zur Lehre des Herzens im klassischen Altertum," *Janus,* 15, p. 797, 1910.

PARSONS, E.A. *The Alexandrinian Library,* London, Cleaver and Hume, 1952.

SUDHOFF, K. "Aegyptische Mumien," *Arch. Gesch. Med.,* V, 1912.

WALLIS BUDGE, E.A. *The Mummy,* Cambridge Univ. Press, 1925.

WESSETZKY, V. *The Heart Scarab* (Hungarian), Mus. of Arts Press, Budapest, 1934.

WESSETZKY, V. "Egyptian Heart, Egyptian Thought" (Hungarian), *Buvar*, p. 2950, Budapest, 1939.

WILLIAMS, H.S. *A History of Science*, New York, Harper, 1904.

ZURBACH, K. "Vorstellung und Lehren von der Blutbewegung vor Harvey," *Ciba Z.*, *4*, p. 1403, Basel, 1937.

Chapter II.

DAHREMBERG, CH. *Oeuvres Anatomiques, Physiologiques et Medicales de Galien*, Paris, 1857.

GELZER, M. *Caesar der Politiker und Staatsmann*, Munchen, Callwey, 1941.

GIBBON, E. *The Decline and Fall of the Roman Empire*, New York, Viking Press, 1950.

ILBERG, J. *Cornelius Celsus und die Medizin in Rom*, Leipzig, Teubner, 1907.

ILBERG, J. and WELLMAN, M. *Zwei Vortrage zur Gesch. d. antiken Med.*, Berlin, 1911.

KILGOUR, F.G. "Harvey's Use of Galen's Findings in His Discovery," *Journ. Hist. Med. All. Sci.*, *XII*, 1957.

MEISSNER, A. *Altromisches Kulturleben*, Leipzig, Seeman, 1908.

AURELIUS, MARCUS *The Communings With Himself*, New York, Putnam's Sons, 1916.

MEZO, F. *Die Geschichte der Olympischen Spiele*, Budapest, Univ. Press, 1930.

MEYER-STEINEGG, TH. "Die Vivisektion in der antiken Med.", *Monatschr. Wiss. Kunst u. Techn.*, 6, p. 1491, 1911.

MEYER-STEINEGG, TH. "Studien zur Physiol. des Galenos," *Arch. Gesch. Med.*, 5, p. 173, 1912; 6, p. 417, 1913.

MOMMSEN, TH. *The History of Rome*, New York, C. Scribner and Co., 1870.

PLUTARCH *Lives of the Noble Romans*, New York, Dell Publishing Co., 1959.

Chapter III.

ALLESCH, G. *Die Renaissance in Italien*, Weimar, Kiepenhauer, 1912.

BOCCACCIO, G. *Decameron*, New York, The Modern Library, n.d.

BURCKHARDT, J.C. *The Civilization of the Renaissance in Italy,* London, Harrap and Co. Ltd., 1929.

CREUTZ, R. "Die Hochblute der Schule von Salerno," *Dtsch. med. Welt,* p. 1566, 1935.

HADDAD, S.J. and KHAIRALLAH, A.A. "A Forgotten Chapter in the History of the Circulation of the Blood," *Ann. Surg., 104,* p. 1, 1936.

HEYCK, E. *Die Medicier,* Leipzig, Klasing, 1897.

HITTI, P.K. *History of the Arabs,* London, Macmillan, 1951.

HUIZINGA, J. *The Waning of the Middle Ages,* London, Arnold and Co., 1924.

MACHIAVELLI, N. *History of Florence,* New York, The Colonial Press, 1901.

MACKOWSKY, H. *Verrocchio,* Leipzig, Klasing, 1901.

MARCO POLO *Travels,* New York, Garden City Publ. Co., 1926.

MARTI-IBANEZ, F. "Medical Ideas in the Arabian Empire," *Internat. Rec. Med., 168,* 1955.

MARTI-IBANEZ, F. "Maimonides," *Internat. Rec. Med., 165,* 1952.

MEYERHOF, M. "Al Kurashii Ibn Al Nafiis," Leipzig, *Enzykl. d. Islam,* Suppl., 1937.

RATH, G. "Der schwarze Tod," *Ciba Symp., 3,* p. 195, Basel, 1956.

RODWELL, J.M. *The Koran,* London, Dent, 1909.

SARTON, G. *Men of Science in the Renaissance,* Bloomington, Indiana Univ. Press, 1957.

SARTON, G. *Ancient and Medieval Science During the Renaissance,* Philadelphia, Univ. of Penn. Press, 1955.

VASARI, G. *Vite de piu eccellenti pittori,* Firenze, 1556.

WESCHER, P. *Grosskeufleute der Renaissance,* Basel, Holbein, 1941.

Chapter IV.

BELT, E. "Leonardo da Vinci's Studies of the Aging Process," *Geriatrics, 7,* 1952.

BELT, E. "Leonardo da Vinci on the 'Hard Teeth of the Years,'" *Gen. Pract., 19,* 1956.

BELT, E. *Leonardo the Anatomist,* Lawrence Univ. Press, Kansas, 1955.

BOTTAZZI, F. *"L. da Vinci as Physiologist,"* cit. in *L. da Vinci,* London, Cresset, 1957.

DOBY, T. "L. da Vinci on the Heart," *Ther. Hung.,* III, 1953.

DOBY, T. "L. da Vinci's Heart Model and His Studies of the Blood Flow," *J.A.M.A.*, April 1961; *Me. Med. J.*, Jan. 1961.

ESCHE, S. *L. da Vinci, das anatomische Werk*, Basel, Holbein, 1954.

FAVARO, G. "L. da Vinci as Anatomist," cit. *L. da Vinci*, London, Cresset, 1957.

FREUD, S. *L. da Vinci, a Study in Psychosexuality*, New York, Random House, 1947.

HEKLER, A. *L. da Vinci* (Hungarian), Budapest, Atheneum, 1930.

HENSZELMAN, I. *L. da Vinci* (Hungarian), Budapest, Revai, 1892.

KEELE, K.D. *L. da Vinci on Movement of the Heart and Blood*, London, Harvey and Blythe, 1952.

L. DA VINCI *Quaderni d' anatomia I-VI*, Christiania, J. Dybwad, 1911-1916.

L. DA VINCI *Drawings and Notes*, Code Leicester.

L. DA VINCI *Codice Atlantico*, Milano, Hoepli, 1894-1904.

L. DA VINCI *Del'anatomia fogli A*, Paris, Rouvyere, 1898.

L. DA VINCI *Dell'anatomia fogli B*, Torino, Roux e Viarengo, 1901.

L. DA VINCI *Drawings in Windsor Castle*, Cambridge, K. Clark, 1935.

L. DA VINCI *Les Manuscrits de l'Institut de France A-M*, Paris, Ravaisson-Mollien, 1883.

L. DA VINCI *Oxford Drawings*.

L. DA VINCI *Trattato della pittura*, London, Bell, 1910.

LUCKE, TH. *L. da Vinci, Tagebucher und Aufzeichnungen*, Berlin, Akadem. Verl., 1940.

LUDECKE, H. *L. da Vinci im Spiegel seiner Zeit*, Berlin, Acad. Sc. Press, 1953.

LYKA, K. *History of Arts* (Hungarian), Budapest, Univ. Press, 1952.

MACCURDY, E. *The Notebooks of L. da Vinci*, New York, Garden City Publ. Co., 1941.

MACHIAVELLI, N. *The Prince*, New York, Oxford Univ. Press, 1952.

MARTI-IBANEZ, F. "The Artist as Physician," *Intern. Rec. Med.*, *167*, 1954.

PIANTANIDA, G. *L. da Vinci*, Milano, Hoepli, 1939.

RICHTER, J.P. *The Literary Works of L. da Vinci*, New York, Oxford Univ. Press, 1939.

ROLLAND, R. *Michelangelo*, New York, Boni, 1935.

SABATINI, R. *The Life of Cesare Borgia*, Boston and New York, Houghton Mifflin, 1924.

SEIDLITZ, W. *L. da Vinci*, Wien, Phaidon, 1935.

SOLMI, ED. *Le fonti dei manuscritti di L. da Vinci*, Giorn. d. Lett. Ital., Torino, 1908.

Chapter V.

BRANDI, K.   *Kaiser Karl V.*, Munchen, Bruckman, 1937.
BRODRICK, J.   *Saint Frances Xavier*, London, Burns Oates, 1952.
CASTIGLIONI, A.   "Die Schule von Padua . . .", *Ciba Z.*, *11*, p. 4446. 1950.
CHLEDOWSKY, C.   *Rom, die Menschen der Renaissance*, Munchen, Muller, 1922.
CUSHING, HARVEY   *A Bio-bibliography of A. Vesalius*, New York, Schuman, 1943.
FULTON, J.F.   "A. Vesale, Fondateur de l'Anatomie Moderne", *Rev. Quest. Sci.*, p. 161, 1952.
HINTZSCHE, E.   "A Vesal und sein Werk," *Ciba Z.*, *9*, p. 3655, 1946.
HINTZSCHE, E.   "Der Kampf um die vesalische Anatomie," *Ciba Z.*, *9*, p. 3663, 1946.
PARIS, P.   *Etudes sur Francois I*, Paris, 1891.
ROTH, M.   *Andreas Vesalius*, Berlin, Reimer, 1892.
SCHWARZFELD, G.   *Charles V., Father of Europe*, Chicago, Regnery, 1957.
SUDHOFF, K.   *Paracelsus*, Leipzig, Bibliogr. Inst. 1936.
VESALIUS, A.   *De humani corporis fabrica*, Basel, Oporini, 1543.
VESALIUS, A.   *Epistola de radicis chynae*, Basel, Oporini, 1546.
WOLF-HEIDEGGER, G.   "Die medizinische Fakultat Basel," *Ciba Symp.*, *6*, p. 243, 1959.

Chapter VI.

BAINTON, R.H.   *Hunted Heretic*, Boston, The Beacon Press, 1953.
BECKER, B.   *Autour de M. Servet et de S. Castellion*, Haarlem, Willink and Zoon, 1953.
Corpus Reformatorum   Archives cit. by P. Pruzsinszky.
DIDE, A.   *Michel Servet et Calvin*, Paris, Flamarion, 1897.
DOBY, T.   *Zur Entdeckung des kleinen Kreislaufes*, Basel, Cardiologia, 1958.
LADAME, P.   *Michel Servet*, Vienne, 1915.
LEJEUNE, F.   "Francesco Reina," *Munch. Med. W.*, p. 21, 1923.
MALLEY, CH.D.   *Michel Servetus*, London, Lloyd-Luke, 1953.
PRUZINSZKY, P.   *Calvin* (Hungarian) Ref. Coll. Press, 1909.
TOLLIN, H.   *Michel Servet*, Paris, 1879.
TOLLIN, H.   "Kritische Bemerkungen uber Harvey und seine Vorganger"; *Arch. Phys.*, XXVIII, p. 581, 1882.

Tollin, H. *Die Entdeckung des Blutkreislaufes dank Michel Servet,* Jena, Dufft, 1876.

Willis, R. *Servetus and Calvin,* London, Skingt, 1877.

Zurbach, K. "Vorstellungen und Lehren von der Blutbewegung vor Harvey," *Ciba Z.,* Basel, No. 41. 1937.

Zweig, St. *Calvin und Castellion,* Wien, 1936.

Chapter VII.

Arcieri, J.P. *The Circulation of the Blood and A. Cesalpino,* New York, Vanni, 1945.

Cesalpino, A. *Peripateticarum libri V,* Venezia, 1571.

Cesalpino, A. *Questiones medicarum libri II,* Venezia, 1593.

Columbus, R. *De re anatomica libri XV,* Venetiis, Benilaquae, 1559.

Fallopius, G. *Observationes anatomicae,* Venetiis, 1561.

Irsay, S. *Memorie e documenti per la storia dell'Universita di Padova,* Padova, 1922.

Laubry, Ch. *Etude Anatomique du Mouvement du Coeur et du Sang par Harvey,* Paris, Doin, 1950.

Tollin, H. "Vom Septum interventriculare bei Vesalius," *Pfluger's Arch.,* 33, p. 482, 1884.

Toply, R. *Die Bewegung des Herzens und des Blutes von Harvey, mit Anhang aus der Anatomie des R. Colombo,* Leipzig, Barth, 1910.

Vesalius, A. *De humani corporis fabrica,* (Second edition) Basel, Oporini, 1556.

Vesalius, A. *Anatomicarum G. Fallopii Observationum examen,* Venetiis, Franciscis, 1564.

Valverde, J. *Historia de la composicion del cuerpo humano,* Roma, A. Salmanca y A. Hafrerij, 1556.

Chapter VIII

Archivo off. de citta di Venezia, Senator I.R. 45 Terra 1564-65, p. 114.

Aubry, J. *Aubry's Brief Lives,* London, Secker and Warburg, 1949.

Bertoni, G. "Paolo Sarpi anatomico, fisiologo," Siena, *Riv. di storia d. scienze,* XVI, 1923.

Chauvois, L. *W. Harvey, His Life and Times,* New York, Philos. Libr., 1957.

Durant, W. *The Story of Philosophy,* New York, 1927.

Fabricius ab Aquapendente *De venarum ostiolis,* Patavii, 1603.

FRANKLIN, K.J.   *Harvey De motu cordis etc.,* Oxford, Blackwell, 1957.
FRANKLIN, K.J.   *A monograph on Veins,* Springfield, Ill., C. Thomas, 1937.
FULTON, J.F.   *Physiology,* New York, Hoeber, 1931.
HARVEY, W.   *Exercitatio anatomica de motu cordis et sanguinis in animalibus,* Francofurti, Fitzer, 1628.
HARVEY, W.   *Exercitatio anatomica secunda et tertia de circulatione sanguinis ad Joannem Riolanum filium,* Roterodami 1649.
HARVEY, W.   *Exercitationes de generatione animalium,* London, 1651.
HEMMETER, J.C.   "The History of the Circulation of the Blood,"*J. Hopkins Hosp. Bull,* XVI, No. 170, 1905.
IZQUIEDRO, J.J.   *Harvey iniciador del metodo esperimentale,* Mexico, 1936.
LERICHE, R.   *Embolisme des Arteres,* Paris, Masson, 1943.
KILGOUR, F.G.   *W. Harvey's Use of the Quantitative Method,* Yale J. Biol. and Med., *26,* 1954.
MACAULAY, TH.B.   *Francis Bacon,* New York, Longmans, 1914.
MARTI-IBANEZ, F.   "Padua and London," *Internat. Rac. Med., 170,* 1957.
MILFORD, H.   *Portraits of Dr. W. Harvey,* New York, Oxford Univ. Press, 1913.
PAYNE, J.F.   *Notes to Accompany ... the Diploma of Padua of W. Harvey,* London, Chiswick Press, 1908.
PELLER, S.   "Harvey's and Cesalpino's Role in the History of Medicine," *Bull. Hist. Med.,* XXIII, p. 213, 1949.
POWER, D'ARCY   *William Harvey,* London, Fisher, 1897.
PRIMOROSIUS, J.   *Exercitationes et animadversiones in librum de motu cordis ...,* London, 1630.
RICHET, CH.   *Histoire de la Circulation,* Aesculape, 1926.
RIOLANUS, J.   *Enchidrium anatomicum et pathologicum,* Paris, Meturas, 1648.
SAINT-GERMAIN, B.   *Déscartes, Consideré comme Physiologist et Médecin,* Paris, Masson, 1869.
SANTILLANA, G.   *The Crime of Galileo,* Chicago, Univ. Press, 1955.
SCOTT, E.   *Six Stuart Sovereigns,* London, G. Allen and Unwin Ltd., 1935.
SINGER, C.J.   *The Discovery of the Circulation of the Blood,* London, G. Bell and Sons, 1922.
TREVELYAN, G.M.   *History of England Under the Stuarts,* New York, Putnam, 1912.

WALAEUS, J. *Epistola de motu chyli et sanguinis ad Th. Bartholinum*, 1641.

WILSON, J.D. *Life in Shakespeare's England*, Cambridge Univ. Press, 1911.

Chapter IX.

BENEDICENTI, A. *Malati, medici e pharmacisti*, Milano, Hoepli, 1924.

BUESS, H. "Die Geschichte der Atmungslehre," *Ciba Z.*, *91*, Basel, 1943.

FULTON J.F. "Discovery of the Capillaries," *Circulation Proc.*, Springfield, Ill., C. Thomas, 1958.

DE FRANCESCO, G. "Die medizinische Fakultat der Universitat Bologna," *Ciba Z.*, *81*, Basel, 1941.

HINTZSCHE, E. "Die Anfange der mikroskopischen Anatomie," *Ciba Z.*, *110*, Basel, 1948.

HINTZCHE, E. "Mikroskope aus dem 17. und 18. Jahrhundert, *Ciba Z.*, *117*, Basel, 1949.

MACCALLUM, W.G. "Marcello Malpighi," *Johns Hopkins Hosp. Bull.* *16*, p. 275, 1905.

MAJOR, R.H. *A History of Medicine*, Springfield, Ill., Thomas, 1954.

MALPIGHI, M. *De pulmonibus epistolae II ad Borellium*, Bologna, 1661.

MALPIGHI, M. *De viscerum structura*, London, J. Martin, 1669.

MALPIGHI, M. *Opera Omnia*, London, T. Sawbridge, 1686.

MALPIGHI, M. *Opera posthuma*, London, A. and J. Churchill, 1697.

MALPIGHI, M. *Autobiographia* (see Benedicenti).

MATTHEWS, B. *Molière, His Life and Works*, New York, C. Scribner's Sons, 1910.

MOLIERE, *Le Malade imaginaire* (1673).

MUNSTER, L. *M. Malpighi* (Hungarian), Orv. U. Budapest, 1935.

RAMON, FERNANDEZ, *Molière*, New York, Hill and Wang, 1958.

NAME INDEX

■

Abd al-Latiif, 54

Alaric, (c. 370-410 A.D.) 52, 251

Alberti, Leone Battista (1404-1472), 68-69, 73, 251

Albertus Magnus (1206?-1280), 124, 251

Alexander the Great (356-323 B.C.), 3, 11, 13, 251

Alexander VI, Pope (1430-1503), 84, 251

Al Geber, 177

Al Nafiis (13th century), 54, 145, 252
  anatomical studies, 55-56
  refutes Galen, 56-61
  views on circulation, 167

Anaxagoras (c. 500-430 B.C.), 252

Anghiera, Pietro Martyr d', 134, 252

Andernach, Günther von, 114, 116, 127-128, 132, 134, 138, 139, 257

Antiochus (325-261 B.C.), 10-11, 252

Archimedes (287-212 B.C.), 29, 252

Argyropoulos (1415-1487), 68, 252

Aristarchus of Samos (c. 310-230 B.C.), 19, 28, 252

Aristotle (c. 384-322 B.C.), 1, 3ff., 9, 19, 38, 55, 126, 158, 192, 200, 240, 252
  portrait, 4
  views on physiology, 5ff., 10

Asclepiades (died c. 40 B.C.), 35, 252

Attila (406-453 A.D.), 52, 252

Augustus (See Caesar)

Aurelianus, Lucius Domitius (c. 213-275 A.D.), 52, 253

Avicenna (See Ibn Sina)

Bacon, Sir Francis, 189, 201-203, 207, 253
  influence on Harvey, 190

Bacon, Roger, 62-63, 253

Baersdorf, Cornelius, 253

275

SUBJECT INDEX

Alexandria, 30
  under the Ptolemies, 12-14, 18-20
  library, 28
    burned (46 B.C.), 31
    burned (389 A.D.) 53
Anatomy:
  early Greek teaching, 5-10
  Aristotle's views, 5-6, 10
  early Egyptian views, 17
  Herophilus' observations, 20-22
  Erasistratus' ideas, 23-25
  Galen's conclusions, 39-44, 48, 50
  Leonardo da Vinci's studies, 75-79, 85-86, 88-89, 92-95, 97, 99, 101
  Vesalius' research, 119-129, 168
  Servetus' writings, 141-147, 167-168
  Valverde's book, 166, 168
  Columbus' work, 166-168
  Cesalpino's work, 169-173
  Fallopia's book, 175ff

Fabricius' teachings, 182-186
  Harvey's research, 203-207, 219, 220, 228-229
  Malpighi's research, 224-235, 240, 247
Aorta (See Circulatory System and Heart)
Art of Love, The, (Maimonides), 56
Arteries (See Circulatory System)
Astrology, 138-139
Astronomy, Aristotle's deductions, 5n.
  Aristarchs' estimates, 19, 28
  Eratosthenes' calculations, 28-29
  during Renaissance, 65
  Leonardo da Vinci's notes, 87
  Copernicus' theories, 106
  The Church's influence, 107, 196
  Galileo's discoveries, 191, 196, 202
Auricles (See Heart)
Autopsy, beginnings, 160
Basel, University of, 110-111